REVISE C4

for MEI Structured Mathematics

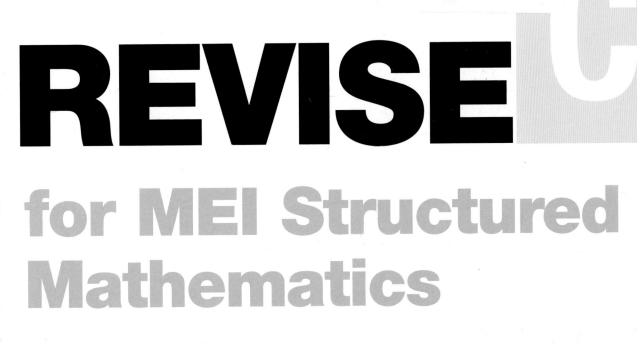

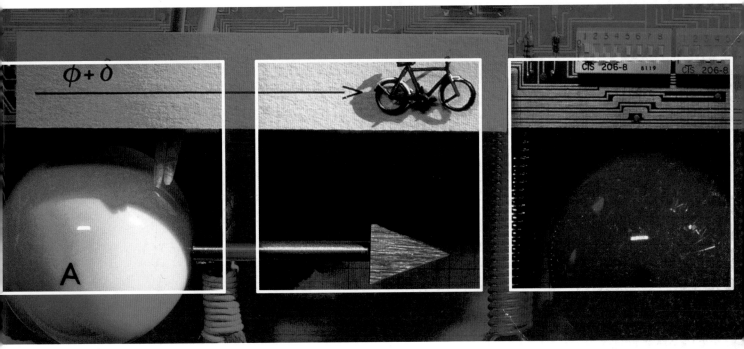

Series Editor
Roger Porkess

Authors
Catherine Berry, Diana Boynova, Sophie Goldie, David Holland, Maureen Sheehan, David Smart

HODDER EDUCATION
AN HACHETTE UK COMPANY

Every effort has been made to trace all copyright holders, but if any have been inadvertently overlooked the Publishers will be pleased to make the necessary arrangements at the first opportunity.

Although every effort has been made to ensure that website addresses are correct at time of going to press, Hodder Education cannot be held responsible for the content of any website mentioned in this book. It is sometimes possible to find a relocated web page by typing in the address of the home page for a website in the URL window of your browser.

Hachette UK's policy is to use papers that are natural, renewable and recyclable products and made from wood grown in sustainable forests. The logging and manufacturing processes are expected to conform to the environmental regulations of the country of origin.

Orders: please contact Bookpoint Ltd, 130 Milton Park, Abingdon, Oxon OX14 4SB.
Telephone: (44) 01235 827720. Fax: (44) 01235 400454. Lines are open 9.00 – 5.00, Monday to Saturday, with a 24-hour message answering service.
Visit our website at www.hoddereducation.co.uk

© Catherine Berry, Diana Boynova, Sophie Goldie, David Holland,
Maureen Sheehan, David Smart, 2009
First published in 2009 by
Hodder Education,
An Hachette UK Company
Carmelite House, 50 Victoria Embankment,
London EC4Y 0DZ

Impression number   7
Year   2015

Personal Tutor © Catherine Berry, Diana Boynova, Sophie Goldie, David Holland,
Roger Porkess, Maureen Sheehan, David Smart, 2009; with contributions from Elise Heighway;
developed by Infuze Limited and MMT Limited; cast: Tom Frankland; recorded at Alchemy Soho.

Typeset in 11/12 Helvetica by Tech-Set Ltd., Gateshead, Tyne & Wear
Printed in India

A catalogue record for this title is available from the British Library

ISBN: 978 0 340 957363

Contents

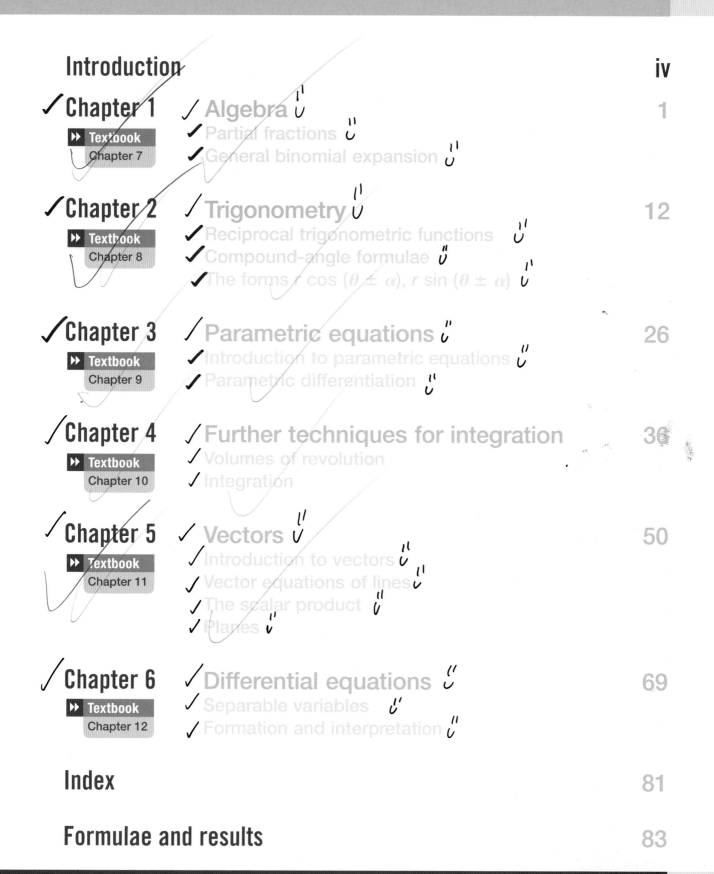

Introduction

Welcome to this Revision Guide for the MEI Core 4 unit!

The book is organised into 15 sections covering the various topics in the syllabus. A typical section is four pages long; the first three pages contain essential information and key worked examples covering the topic.

The last page or two in each section has questions for you to answer so that you can be sure that you have really understood the topic. There is a multiple-choice exercise and an exam-style question. If you are to gain the greatest possible benefit from the book, and so do your best in the Core 4 exam, you should work through these for yourself and then refer to the accompanying website to check your answers.

The multiple-choice questions cover the basic ideas and techniques. It is really important that you work through them carefully; guessing will do you no good at all. When you have decided on the answer you think is right, enter it on the website. If you are right, it tells you so and gives the full solution; check that your answer wasn't just a fluke. If your choice is not right, the website gives you advice about your mistake; the possible wrong answers have all been designed to pick out particular common misunderstandings. The explanations on the website are based on the most likely mistakes; even if you make a different mistake, you will usually find enough help to set you on the right path so that you can try again.

When you come on to the exam-style question, write out your best possible answer. Then go to the website. You will find the solution displayed step-by-step, together with someone talking you through it and giving you helpful advice.

So the book contains the essential information to revise for the exam and, critically, also enables you to check that you have understood it properly. That is a recipe for success.

Finally, a word of warning. This book is designed to be used together with the textbook and not as a replacement for it. This Revision Guide will help you to prepare for the exam but to do really well you also need the deep understanding that comes from the detailed explanations you will find in the textbook.

Good learning and good luck!

Catherine Berry, Diana Boynova, Sophie Goldie, David Holland, Maureen Sheehan, David Smart, Roger Porkess

Where you see the following icon **ƊL**, please refer to the Dynamic Learning Student Online website. Information on how to access this website is printed on the inside front cover of the book.

Accompanying books
MEI Structured Mathematics AS Pure Mathematics C3, C4
ISBN 978 0 340 88851 3

Companion to Advanced Mathematics and Statistics
ISBN 978 0 340 95923 7

Algebra

Partial fractions

A ABOUT THIS TOPIC

In this section you will see how to rewrite in partial fractions an expression $\dfrac{f(x)}{g(x)}$, where $f(x)$ and $g(x)$ are both polynomials. You will also use partial fractions in integration and, in the next section, in binomial expansions.

R REMEMBER

- Algebraic fractions from C1.
- Polynomials from C1.
- Identities from C1.
- Techniques of integration from C3 and C4.

K KEY FACTS

1 **For a polynomial identity** $p(x) \equiv q(x)$

Substituting: for any value of x, say $x = a$, $p(a) = q(a)$.

Equating coefficients: the corresponding coefficients of the polynomials are equal; for example if $ax^2 + bx + c \equiv 3x^2 + 2$, then $a = 3$, $b = 0$ and $c = 2$.

2 **Some partial fraction patterns**

(Note that any coefficients on the top lines of the fractions on the right may be zero.)

- $\dfrac{px + q}{(ax + b)(cx + d)} \equiv \dfrac{A}{ax + b} + \dfrac{B}{cx + d}$ where $a \neq 0$, $c \neq 0$ and $ax + b \neq k(cx + d)$

- $\dfrac{px + q}{(ax + b)^2} \equiv \dfrac{A}{ax + b} + \dfrac{B}{(ax + b)^2}$ where $a \neq 0$

- $\dfrac{px^2 + qx + r}{(ax + b)(cx^2 + d)} \equiv \dfrac{A}{ax + b} + \dfrac{Bx + C}{cx^2 + d}$ where $a \neq 0$ and $c \neq 0$

- $\dfrac{px^2 + qx + r}{(ax + b)(cx + d)^2} \equiv \dfrac{A}{ax + b} + \dfrac{B}{cx + d} + \dfrac{C}{(cx + d)^2}$ where $a \neq 0$, $c \neq 0$ and $ax + b \neq k(cx + d)$

  Although you will usually use the form above, this rational function has an alternative partial fraction pattern that could be given in an examination question:

  $\dfrac{px^2 + qx + r}{(ax + b)(cx + d)^2} \equiv \dfrac{A}{ax + b} + \dfrac{Bx + D}{(cx + d)^2}$ where $a \neq 0$, $c \neq 0$ and $ax + b \neq k(cx + d)$

3 **Examples of the types of integrals you will need to use with partial fractions**

- $\displaystyle\int \frac{7}{3x + 5}\,dx \equiv \frac{7}{3}\int \frac{3}{3x + 5}\,dx = \frac{7}{3}\ln|3x + 5| + k$

- $\displaystyle\int \frac{7x}{3x^2 + 5}\,dx \equiv \frac{7}{2 \times 3}\int \frac{2 \times 3 \times x}{3x^2 + 5}\,dx = \frac{7}{6}\ln|3x^2 + 5| + k$

- $\displaystyle\int \frac{7}{(3x + 5)^2}\,dx = -\frac{7}{3(3x + 5)} + k$

General note

Partial fractions are a way of changing the form of an expression to one that may make it easier to apply a required technique; for example, binomial expansion or integration. The form is not **simpler** but it is **more appropriate** for the technique you are about to use.

A | ADVICE

There are more partial fraction patterns than those required for C4 and you meet these in more advanced work.

A | ADVICE

A *rational expression* (also called a *rational function*) is an algebraic fraction of the form $\frac{f(x)}{g(x)}$ where $f(x)$ and $g(x)$ are both polynomials.

A rational expression is a *proper* fraction if the degree of the top line (numerator) is less than that of the bottom line (denominator); otherwise the fraction is *improper*. For instance, $\frac{x+1}{x^2+1}$ is a *proper rational expression* but $\frac{x^2+x+1}{x^2+1}$ is not.

The patterns in **Key facts** cover only proper rational expressions.

The general method for putting a proper rational function into partial fractions is outlined in steps **(A)** to **(D)** in Example 1.

✓ **EXAMPLE 1** Express $\frac{x-1}{x^2+x}$ in terms of the sum of partial fractions.

SOLUTION

(A) Fully factorise the bottom line (denominator)

The denominator is $x^2 + x$.

Factorising gives $x(x + 1)$.

(B) Select the appropriate partial fraction pattern shown in Key facts 2

The required pattern for $\frac{x-1}{x(x+1)}$ is

> Note that A and B are constants to be determined. On the left-hand side the bottom line is written in factorised form.

$$\frac{px+q}{(ax+b)(cx+d)} \equiv \frac{A}{ax+b} + \frac{B}{cx+d} \text{ with } p=1, q=-1, a=1, b=0, c=1 \text{ and } d=1.$$

This gives $\dfrac{x-1}{x(x+1)} \equiv \dfrac{A}{x} + \dfrac{B}{x+1}$

(C) Multiply through by the denominator of the rational function to clear all fractions

Multiply all the terms by $x(x + 1)$.

This gives $\dfrac{x-1}{x(x+1)} \times x(x+1) \equiv \dfrac{A}{x} \times x(x+1) + \dfrac{B}{(x+1)} \times x(x+1)$

so $x - 1 \equiv A(x + 1) + Bx$.

(D) Use one or both of the methods of *Substitution* or *Comparing coefficients* to find the values of the constants

In this example only Substitution is required.

Find the value(s) of x that make the expression found in **(A)** come to zero.

The expression is $x(x + 1)$ so these values are $x = 0$ and $x = -1$.

Substitute $x = 0$ in $x - 1 \equiv A(x + 1) + Bx$.

This gives
$$0 - 1 = A \times (0 + 1) + B \times 0$$
$$\Rightarrow -1 = A$$
$$\Rightarrow A = -1$$

> Note that this is an equation not an identity.

Substitute $x = -1$ in $x - 1 \equiv A(x + 1) + Bx$.

This gives
$$(-1) - 1 = A \times 0 + B \times (-1)$$
$$\Rightarrow -2 = -B$$
$$\Rightarrow B = 2$$

> $x + 1 = 0$

Hence
$$\frac{x - 1}{x(x + 1)} \equiv -\frac{1}{x} + \frac{2}{x + 1}$$

The next examples refer to the same steps **(A)** to **(D)** without quoting them.

✓ **EXAMPLE 2**   Express $\dfrac{x - 2}{x^3 - 2x^2 + x}$ as the sum of partial fractions.

SOLUTION

(A) Factorising gives $x^3 - 2x^2 + x \equiv x(x^2 - 2x + 1) \equiv x(x - 1)^2$.

(B) The appropriate form for the partial fractions is
$$\frac{x - 2}{x(x - 1)^2} \equiv \frac{A}{x} + \frac{B}{x - 1} + \frac{C}{(x - 1)^2}$$

(C) Multiply all the terms by $x(x - 1)^2$. This gives
$$\frac{x - 2}{x(x - 1)^2} \times x(x - 1)^2$$
$$\equiv \frac{A}{x} \times x(x - 1)^2 + \frac{B}{x - 1} \times x(x - 1)^2 + \frac{C}{(x - 1)^2} \times x(x - 1)^2$$
so $x - 2 \equiv A(x - 1)^2 + Bx(x - 1) + Cx$

(D) You cannot solve this identity using only substitution. It may be solved by equating coefficients and this method is used here.

Expanding the brackets on the right-hand side gives
$$x - 2 \equiv A(x^2 - 2x + 1) + B(x^2 - x) + Cx$$

and this may be written as
$$x - 2 \equiv x^2(A + B) + x(-2A - B + C) + A$$

> Note that these are equations not identities.

Equating the coefficients of x^2: $0 = A + B$ ①

Equating the coefficients of x: $1 = -2A - B + C$ ... ②

Equating the constant terms: $-2 = A$ ... ③

From ③ $A = -2$.

Substituting for A in ① gives $B = 2$.

Substituting for A and B in ② gives $1 = -2 \times (-2) - 2 + C$ so $C = -1$.

Hence $\dfrac{x-2}{x(x-1)^2} \equiv -\dfrac{2}{x} + \dfrac{2}{x-1} - \dfrac{1}{(x-1)^2}$.

A ADVICE

All the partial fractions required for C4 may be worked using **only** the equating coefficients method for solving identities. However, there is often less working required if substitution is used.

Here is another way of solving the identity at step **(D)** in Example 2:

$$x - 2 \equiv A(x-1)^2 + Bx(x-1) + Cx$$

The values of x that make terms on the right-hand side zero are

$$x = 0 \text{ and } x = 1.$$

Substitute $x = 0$ and you get

$$0 - 2 = A(0-1)^2 + B \times 0 + C \times 0$$

> The 2nd and 3rd terms both contain an x factor and so must be zero as $x = 0$.

so $\quad -2 = A + 0 + 0$ and $A = -2$.

Substitute $x = 1$ and you get

$$1 - 2 = A \times 0 + B \times 0 + C \times 1$$

> The 1st and 2nd terms both contain an $x - 1$ factor and so must be zero as $x = 1$.

so $\quad -1 = 0 + 0 + C$ and $C = -1$.

Now you only have to find B. To do this you equate the coefficients of one of the terms involving B. This can be the x^2 or the x term.

Comparing the coefficient of x^2 in

$$x - 2 \equiv A(x-1)^2 + Bx(x-1) + Cx$$

> There is no need to expand the brackets and rearrange the terms as you can see by inspection that B is in the coefficient of x^2 and in the coefficient of x.

gives $\quad 0 = A + B$

since $\quad A = -2, B = 2$.

A ADVICE

As in the working above, it is often possible to use inspection to compare coefficients. It is always best if you can use a coefficient that involves only one constant you do not know.

A ADVICE

Substituting $x = 0$ in an identity is always easy and is equivalent to comparing the constant terms. Of course, there is no point in substituting $x = 0$ **and** comparing the constant terms as you will obtain the same equations.

Using partial fractions in integration

Using partial fractions to change the 'shape' of an expression may let you rewrite an integral in a form which makes it clear what to do next. This is illustrated in the next example.

EXAMPLE 3 Evaluate $\int_2^3 \dfrac{1}{6x^2 - 3x}\,\mathrm{d}x$.

SOLUTION

First you express the integral in partial fractions. Follow the steps as above.

(A) Factorising gives $6x^2 - 3x \equiv 3x(2x - 1)$.

(B) The appropriate form is $\dfrac{1}{3x(2x - 1)} \equiv \dfrac{A}{3x} + \dfrac{B}{(2x - 1)}$.

(C) Multiply all the terms by $3x(2x - 1)$. This gives

$$\frac{1}{\cancel{3x(2x-1)}} \times \cancel{3x(2x-1)}$$

$$\equiv \frac{A}{\cancel{3x}} \times 3\cancel{x}(2x - 1) + \frac{B}{\cancel{(2x-1)}} \times 3x\cancel{(2x-1)}$$

so $1 \equiv A(2x - 1) + B(3x)$.

(D) The values of x that make terms on the right-hand side come to zero are $x = \frac{1}{2}$ and $x = 0$.

Substitute $x = \frac{1}{2}$ $\qquad 1 = 0 + B\left(3 \times \frac{1}{2}\right) \Rightarrow B = \frac{2}{3}$

Substitute $x = 0$ $\qquad\qquad 1 = A(-1) + 0 \Rightarrow A = -1$

Hence $\dfrac{1}{3x(2x - 1)} \equiv \dfrac{-1}{3x} + \dfrac{\frac{2}{3}}{(2x - 1)}$

> Tidy up as far as possible.

so $\dfrac{1}{3x(2x - 1)} \equiv \dfrac{2}{3(2x - 1)} - \dfrac{1}{3x}$

> Take the $\frac{1}{3}$ outside of the integrals so the top line of each is the derivative of the bottom line. This is the easiest form of the pattern shown in **Key facts**.

Hence $\displaystyle\int_2^3 \frac{1}{6x^2 - 3x}\,\mathrm{d}x = \int_2^3 \frac{2}{3(2x - 1)}\,\mathrm{d}x - \int_2^3 \frac{1}{3x}\,\mathrm{d}x$

$$= \frac{1}{3}\int_2^3 \frac{2}{(2x - 1)}\,\mathrm{d}x - \frac{1}{3}\int_2^3 \frac{1}{x}\,\mathrm{d}x$$

$$= \left[\frac{1}{3}\ln|2x - 1|\right]_2^3 - \left[\frac{1}{3}\ln|x|\right]_2^3$$

> Take out the factor of $\frac{1}{3}$ and express as a single expression to be evaluated.

$$= \frac{1}{3}\left[\ln|2x - 1| - \ln|x|\right]_2^3$$

$$= \frac{1}{3}\left[\ln\left|\frac{2x - 1}{x}\right|\right]_2^3$$

$$= \frac{1}{3}\left[\ln\frac{5}{3} - \ln\frac{3}{2}\right]$$

> Remember the rules of logs:
> $\ln p - \ln q = \ln \dfrac{p}{q}$

$$= \frac{1}{3}\ln\frac{10}{9}$$

$$= 0.0351 \text{ (correct to 3 s.f.)}$$

LINKS

Pure Mathematics	Work with rational functions and series (FP1, FP2, DE).
	Applications of calculus (FP2, DE).
Mechanics	Work with rational functions and series (M3, M4).
	Applications of calculus (M3, M4).

Test Yourself ◗L

1 Which of the following is the correct form of partial fractions for the expression $\dfrac{x}{x^2 - 3x - 4}$?

A $\dfrac{A}{x+4} + \dfrac{B}{x-1}$

B $\dfrac{Ax}{x+1} + \dfrac{Bx}{x-4}$

C $\dfrac{Ax+B}{x^2-3x-4}$

D $\dfrac{A}{x+1} + \dfrac{B}{x-4}$

2 Express $\dfrac{4 + 6x - x^2}{(x-1)(x+2)^2}$ as the sum of partial fractions.

A $\dfrac{1}{x-1} + \dfrac{4}{(x+2)^2}$

B $\dfrac{1}{x-1} - \dfrac{2}{x+2} + \dfrac{4}{(x+2)^2}$

C $\dfrac{1}{x-1} - \dfrac{2}{x+2} + \dfrac{4}{3(x+2)^2}$

D $\dfrac{6}{x+2} + \dfrac{4}{(x+2)^2} - \dfrac{1}{x-1}$

3 Express $\dfrac{8x^2 + 9x - 4}{(2x^2 + 1)(x-3)}$ as the sum of partial fractions.

A $\dfrac{-2x+3}{2x^2+1} + \dfrac{5}{x-3}$

B $\dfrac{-2x}{2x^2+1} + \dfrac{5}{x-3}$

C $\dfrac{3}{2x^2+1} + \dfrac{5}{x-3}$

D $\dfrac{5}{x-3} - \dfrac{2x+3}{2x^2+1}$

4 Express $\dfrac{5-x}{x^2-x-2}$ in partial fractions and use these to find $\displaystyle\int\left(\dfrac{5-x}{x^2-x-2}\right)dx$.

A $\ln\left(\dfrac{|x-2|}{(x+1)^4}\right) + c$

B $\ln|x-2| + 2\ln|x+1| + c$

C $\ln\left(\dfrac{x-2}{(x+1)^2}\right) + c$

D $\ln|x-2| - 2\ln|x+1| + c$

5 Express $\dfrac{5-2x}{(1-x)^2}$ in partial fractions and use these to evaluate $\displaystyle\int_0^{\frac{1}{2}}\left(\dfrac{5-2x}{(1-x)^2}\right)dx$.

A $7\ln 2 - 2$ B $2\ln 2 + 5$ C $2\ln 2 + 3$ D $2\ln 2 - 3$

Exam-Style Question ◗L

i) Express $\dfrac{3x-2}{(2x+1)(3x^2+1)}$ in partial fractions.

ii) Hence show that $\displaystyle\int\left(\dfrac{3x-2}{(2x+1)(3x^2+1)}\right)dx = -\ln|2x+1| + \tfrac{1}{2}\ln|3x^2+1| + c$.

iii) Show that $\displaystyle\int\left(\dfrac{3x-2}{(2x+1)(3x^2+1)}\right)dx$ may be written as $\ln\left(\dfrac{A\sqrt{3x^2+1}}{|2x+1|}\right)$.

General binomial expansion

A · ABOUT THIS TOPIC

You learnt how to find the binomial expansion of expressions such as $(x + 2)^6$ in C1. You only expanded binomial expressions which were raised to a positive, integer power. In this section you will learn how to use the binomial theorem to find the expansion of expressions such as $(1 + x)^{-2}$ or $(2 - 3x)^{\frac{1}{2}}$.

R · REMEMBER

- Binomial theorem and expansions from C1.
- Factorials from C1.
- Laws of indices from C1.

K · KEY FACTS

- The binomial theorem states:
$$(1 + x)^n = 1 + nx + \frac{n(n - 1)}{2!}x^2 + \frac{n(n - 1)(n - 2)}{3!}x^3 + \dots$$
when $n \in \mathbb{N}$, x may take any value
but when $n \notin \mathbb{N}$, $|x| < 1$.

- You can rewrite $(a + x)^n$ as $a^n\left(1 + \dfrac{x}{a}\right)^n$.

In C1 you learnt that the binomial expansion of $(1 + x)^n$ is

$$(1 + x)^n = 1 + nx + \frac{n(n - 1)}{2!}x^2 + \frac{n(n - 1)(n - 2)}{3!}x^3 + \dots$$

> The dots show that the expansion continues like this.

You can also use this expansion when n is a fraction or is negative.

> n could be -2 or $\frac{1}{2}$.

However, when n is not a positive integer ($x \notin \mathbb{N}$) the expansion is only valid when $|x| < 1$.

> For values of x between -1 and 1.

As the expansion is infinite you will only be asked to find the first few terms.

✓ EXAMPLE 1

Find the first four terms in the expansion of $(1 + x)^{-5}$ in ascending powers of x.

State the values of x for which the expansion is valid.

SOLUTION

Use $(1 + x)^n = 1 + nx + \dfrac{n(n - 1)}{2!}x^2 + \dfrac{n(n - 1)(n - 2)}{3!}x^3 + \dots$ when $|x| < 1$.

> Remember that 1 is a term too!

Replace n with -5

> Watch your signs and take care when you subtract 1 from a negative number.

$$(1 + x)^{-5} = 1 + (-5)x + \frac{(-5)(-6)}{2!}x^2 + \frac{(-5)(-6)(-7)}{3!}x^3 + \dots$$

> Remember $3! = 3 \times 2 \times 1$.

Tidying this up gives

$$(1 + x)^{-5} = 1 - 5x + 15x^2 - 35x^3 + \dots$$

So $(1 + x)^{-5} \approx 1 - 5x + 15x^2 - 35x^3$ when $|x| < 1$

 Notice the use of the $\approx$ sign. When you use 3 dots (...) you are saying that the expansion carries on further so the expression on the left-hand side has exactly the same value as the one on the right-hand side. However, when you just give the first few terms of the expansion (without the 3 dots) then the two expressions are no longer exactly equal and so you need to write '$\approx$' instead of '='.

✓ EXAMPLE 2

Write down the first three terms in the binomial expansion of $\dfrac{1}{\sqrt{1 - 2x}}$ in ascending powers of x.

For what range of values of x is this expansion valid?

SOLUTION

You can write $\dfrac{1}{\sqrt{1 - 2x}}$ as $(1 - 2x)^{-\frac{1}{2}}$.

Use $(1 + x)^n = 1 + nx + \dfrac{n(n - 1)}{2!}x^2 + \dfrac{n(n - 1)(n - 2)}{3!}x^3 + \dots$ when $|x| < 1$

Replace x with $(-2x)$ and n with $-\dfrac{1}{2}$

$$(1 - 2x)^{-\frac{1}{2}} = 1 + \left(-\tfrac{1}{2}\right)(-2x) + \frac{\left(-\tfrac{1}{2}\right)\left(-\tfrac{3}{2}\right)}{2!}(-2x)^2 + \dots$$

> You need to divide both sides of the inequality by 2 as you are asked for the range of values of x, not $2x$.

Tidying this up gives

$$(1 - 2x)^{-\frac{1}{2}} = 1 + x + \tfrac{3}{2}x^2 + \dots \text{ when } |2x| < 1$$

So $\dfrac{1}{\sqrt{1 - 2x}} \approx 1 + x + \tfrac{3}{2}x^2$ when $|x| < \tfrac{1}{2}$

> This means $-\tfrac{1}{2} < x < \tfrac{1}{2}$.

Sometimes you are asked to expand an expression which is not in the form $(1 + x)^n$. When this happens you need to rearrange the expression so that the first term inside the brackets is 1 **before** you expand it.

✓ EXAMPLE 3

i)   Find a quadratic approximation for $\sqrt{16 - x^2}$, stating the range of values of x for which this expansion is valid.
ii)   Use your expansion to find an approximation for $\sqrt{15.9}$.

SOLUTION

i)   You can write $\sqrt{16 - x^2}$ as $\left(16 - \dfrac{16x^2}{16}\right)^{\frac{1}{2}}$

> Now you have '16' in both terms and so you can take out $16^{\frac{1}{2}}$ as a common factor.

So $(16 - x^2)^{\frac{1}{2}} = 16^{\frac{1}{2}}\left(1 - \dfrac{x^2}{16}\right)^{\frac{1}{2}}$

$$= 4\left(1 - \dfrac{x^2}{16}\right)^{\frac{1}{2}}$$

> In general:
> $$(a + x)^n = a^n\left(1 + \dfrac{x}{a}\right)^n$$

Use $(1 + x)^n = 1 + nx + \dfrac{n(n - 1)}{2!}x^2 + \dfrac{n(n - 1)(n - 2)}{3!}x^3 + \dots$

when $|x| < 1$.

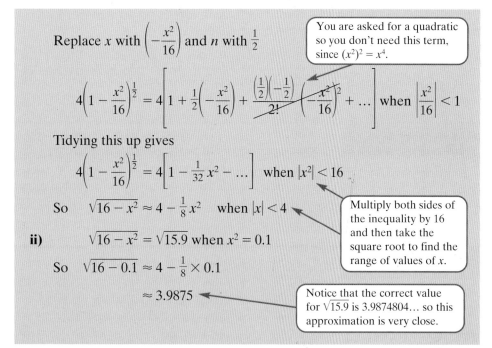

Replace x with $\left(-\dfrac{x^2}{16}\right)$ and n with $\dfrac{1}{2}$

> You are asked for a quadratic so you don't need this term, since $(x^2)^2 = x^4$.

$$4\left(1 - \frac{x^2}{16}\right)^{\frac{1}{2}} = 4\left[1 + \frac{1}{2}\left(-\frac{x^2}{16}\right) + \frac{\left(\frac{1}{2}\right)\left(-\frac{1}{2}\right)}{2!}\left(-\frac{x^2}{16}\right)^2 + \dots\right] \text{ when } \left|\frac{x^2}{16}\right| < 1$$

Tidying this up gives

$$4\left(1 - \frac{x^2}{16}\right)^{\frac{1}{2}} = 4\left[1 - \frac{1}{32}x^2 - \dots\right] \text{ when } |x^2| < 16$$

So $\quad \sqrt{16 - x^2} \approx 4 - \frac{1}{8}x^2 \quad$ when $|x| < 4$

> Multiply both sides of the inequality by 16 and then take the square root to find the range of values of x.

ii) $\qquad \sqrt{16 - x^2} = \sqrt{15.9}$ when $x^2 = 0.1$

So $\quad \sqrt{16 - 0.1} \approx 4 - \frac{1}{8} \times 0.1$

$$\approx 3.9875$$

> Notice that the correct value for $\sqrt{15.9}$ is 3.9874804... so this approximation is very close.

You may have to work with two binomial expansions. Use the tighter restriction when deciding which values of x the overall expansion is valid for.

EXAMPLE 4

Find a, b and c such that $\dfrac{1}{(1 + 3x)(1 - 4x)^2} \approx a + bx + cx^2$.

State the values of x for which the expansion is valid.

SOLUTION

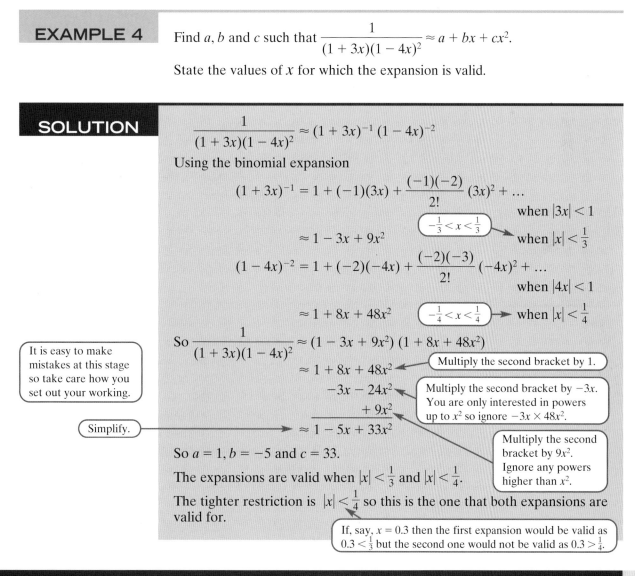

$$\frac{1}{(1 + 3x)(1 - 4x)^2} \approx (1 + 3x)^{-1}(1 - 4x)^{-2}$$

Using the binomial expansion

$$(1 + 3x)^{-1} = 1 + (-1)(3x) + \frac{(-1)(-2)}{2!}(3x)^2 + \dots$$
$$\text{when } |3x| < 1$$
$$-\frac{1}{3} < x < \frac{1}{3}$$
$$\approx 1 - 3x + 9x^2 \qquad \text{when } |x| < \frac{1}{3}$$

$$(1 - 4x)^{-2} = 1 + (-2)(-4x) + \frac{(-2)(-3)}{2!}(-4x)^2 + \dots$$
$$\text{when } |4x| < 1$$
$$\approx 1 + 8x + 48x^2 \qquad -\frac{1}{4} < x < \frac{1}{4} \qquad \text{when } |x| < \frac{1}{4}$$

So $\dfrac{1}{(1 + 3x)(1 - 4x)^2} \approx (1 - 3x + 9x^2)(1 + 8x + 48x^2)$

> It is easy to make mistakes at this stage so take care how you set out your working.

$$\approx 1 + 8x + 48x^2$$

> Multiply the second bracket by 1.

$$-3x - 24x^2$$

> Multiply the second bracket by $-3x$. You are only interested in powers up to x^2 so ignore $-3x \times 48x^2$.

> Simplify.

$$+ 9x^2$$

$$\approx 1 - 5x + 33x^2$$

> Multiply the second bracket by $9x^2$. Ignore any powers higher than x^2.

So $a = 1$, $b = -5$ and $c = 33$.

The expansions are valid when $|x| < \frac{1}{3}$ and $|x| < \frac{1}{4}$.

The tighter restriction is $|x| < \frac{1}{4}$ so this is the one that both expansions are valid for.

> If, say, $x = 0.3$ then the first expansion would be valid as $0.3 < \frac{1}{3}$ but the second one would not be valid as $0.3 > \frac{1}{4}$.

Sometimes you will be asked to rewrite an expression as two or more partial fractions before using the binomial expansion.

The advantage of using partial fractions is that you can add/subtract the resulting expansions rather than multiplying them. It also makes it easier to find the coefficient of one particular term.

EXAMPLE 5

Express $\dfrac{3}{2 - x - x^2}$ in partial fractions.

Hence find the coefficient of x^3 in the binomial expansion of $\dfrac{3}{2 - x - x^2}$ when $|x|$ is small.

SOLUTION

You need to factorise the bottom line

$$\frac{3}{2 - x - x^2} = \frac{3}{(1 - x)(2 + x)}$$

> $2 - x - x^2 = (1 - x)(2 + x)$

Now $\dfrac{3}{(1 - x)(2 + x)} \equiv \dfrac{A}{(1 - x)} + \dfrac{B}{(2 + x)}$

So $\quad 3 \equiv A(2 + x) + B(1 - x)$

> Multiplying both sides by $(1 - x)(2 + x)$.

Let $\quad x = 1 \quad \Rightarrow 3 = 3A \Rightarrow A = 1$

Let $\quad x = -2 \Rightarrow 3 = 3B \Rightarrow B = 1$

This gives

$$\frac{3}{(1 - x)(2 + x)} = \frac{1}{(1 - x)} + \frac{1}{(2 + x)}$$

> To find the binomial approximation you need to **add together** the expansions for $(1 - x)^{-1}$ and $(2 + x)^{-1}$. Don't multiply them!

$$= (1 - x)^{-1} + (2 + x)^{-1}$$

$$= (1 - x)^{-1} + \frac{1}{2}\left(1 + \frac{x}{2}\right)^{-1}$$

> You don't need to write out the whole expansion. You can just use the fact that the term involving x^3 is $\dfrac{n(n - 1)(n - 2)}{3!} x^3$.

Now $\quad (1 - x)^{-1} \approx 1 + (-1)(-x) + \dfrac{(-1)(-2)}{2!}(-x)^2 + \dfrac{(-1)(-2)(-3)}{3!}(-x)^3$

and $\quad \dfrac{1}{2}\left(1 + \dfrac{x}{2}\right)^{-1} \approx \dfrac{1}{2}\left[1 + (-1)\dfrac{x}{2} + \dfrac{(-1)(-2)}{2!}\left(\dfrac{x}{2}\right)^2 + \dfrac{(-1)(-2)(-3)}{3!}\left(\dfrac{x}{2}\right)^3\right]$

So for $(1 - x)^{-1}$ the x^3 term is $\dfrac{(-1)(-2)(-3)}{3!}(-x)^3 = x^3$.

And for $\dfrac{1}{2}\left(1 + \dfrac{x}{2}\right)^{-1}$ the term is $\dfrac{1}{2} \times \dfrac{(-1)(-2)(-3)}{3!}\left(\dfrac{x}{2}\right)^3 = -\dfrac{1}{16}x^3$.

So the term in x^3 is $x^3 + -\dfrac{1}{16}x^3 = \dfrac{15}{16}x^3$.

> Don't forget to multiply by $\dfrac{1}{2}$ as there is $\dfrac{1}{2}$ outside of the bracket.

So the coefficient of x^3 is $\dfrac{15}{16}$.

LINKS

Pure Mathematics   Maclaurin Series (FP2).
Numerical Methods (NM).

Test Yourself ⊃Ⅼ

1 Find the first four terms in the binomial expansion of $(1 - 5x)^{-2}$.

   A $1 + 10x + 75x^2 + 500x^3$ 　　　　　　　B $1 - 10x + 75x^2 - 500x^3$

   C $1 - 2x + 3x^2 - 4x^3$ 　　　　　　　　　D $1 + 10x + 15x^2 + 20x^3$

2 Use the first three terms in the expansion of $\sqrt{1 - x}$ to find an approximation for $\sqrt{0.95}$.
   Write down all of the numbers on your calculator display.

   A 1.0246875 　　　B 0.9746875 　　　C 0.9746796875 　　　D 0.9753125

3 Find a, b and c such that $\dfrac{1}{(1 + 3x)^3} \approx 1 + ax + bx^2 + cx^3$.

   A $a = 9, b = 27$ and $c = 27$ 　　　　　B $a = -3, b = 6$ and $c = -10$

   C $a = -9, b = 18$ and $c = -30$ 　　　　D $a = -9, b = 54$ and $c = -270$

4 Find a quadratic approximation for $\dfrac{1}{\sqrt{4 + x}}$.

   A $1 - \dfrac{1}{2}x + \dfrac{3}{8}x^2$ 　　　　　　　　B $4 - \dfrac{1}{2}x + \dfrac{3}{32}x^2$

   C $\dfrac{1}{2} - \dfrac{1}{16}x + \dfrac{3}{256}x^2$ 　　　　　D $\dfrac{1}{2} - \dfrac{1}{4}x + \dfrac{3}{16}x^2$

5 State the values of x for which the expansion of $\dfrac{1}{\left(1 - \dfrac{x}{2}\right)(4 + 3x)}$ is valid.

   A $|x| < \dfrac{4}{3}$ and $|x| < 2$ 　　B $|x| < \dfrac{4}{3}$ 　　　C $|x| < 1$ 　　　D $|x| < \dfrac{1}{3}$

Exam-Style Question ⊃Ⅼ

i)　Find the first three terms in the binomial expansion of $(1 + y)^{\frac{1}{2}}$ in ascending powers of y.

ii)　Explain why you cannot substitute $y = 4$ into your expansion to provide an estimate for $\sqrt{5}$.

iii)　Find the first three terms in the binomial expansion of $(4 + x)^{\frac{1}{2}}$.
　　State the range of values of x for which the expansion is valid.

iv)　Use your expansion of $(4 + x)^{\frac{1}{2}}$ to find an estimate for $\sqrt{5}$.
　　Using the value of $\sqrt{5}$ on your calculator, find the relative error in your answer.

Trigonometry

2

184
187
201

Reciprocal trigonometric functions

A ABOUT THIS TOPIC

This section extends the work on trigonometry covered in C2 by introducing the reciprocal trigonometrical (trig) functions *cosecant (cosec), secant (sec)* and *cotangent (cot)* and then using them in the solution of a wider range of trig equations.

R REMEMBER

- The three main trig functions, sin, cos and tan, and their graphs from C2.
- The solution of trig equations from C2.
- Radian measure from C2.
- Inverse trig functions and the principal values from C3.
- Binomial expansion from C1 and C4.

K KEY FACTS

Reciprocal trigonometrical functions

1 Definitions

- $\operatorname{cosec} \theta = \dfrac{1}{\sin \theta}$

  where $\theta \neq \ldots, -360°, -180°, 0°, 180°, 360°, \ldots$

- $\sec \theta = \dfrac{1}{\cos \theta}$

  where $\theta \neq \ldots, -270°, -90°, 90°, 270°, \ldots$

- $\cot \theta = \dfrac{1}{\tan \theta}\left(= \dfrac{\cos \theta}{\sin \theta}\right)$

  where $\theta \neq \ldots, -360°, -180°, 0°, 180°, 360°, \ldots$

3 Identities

- $\tan^2 \theta + 1 = \sec^2 \theta$
- $1 + \cot^2 \theta = \operatorname{cosec}^2 \theta$

2 Graphs (the basic trig function is shown as a broken line and the related reciprocal function as a solid line).

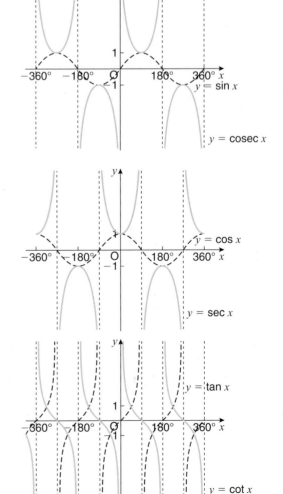

You are familiar with the trig ratios $\sin \theta$, $\cos \theta$ and $\tan \theta$. The reciprocals of these give three more ratios:

$$\frac{1}{\sin \theta} = \operatorname{cosec} \theta, \quad \frac{1}{\cos \theta} = \sec \theta, \quad \frac{1}{\tan \theta} = \cot \theta$$

R RULE

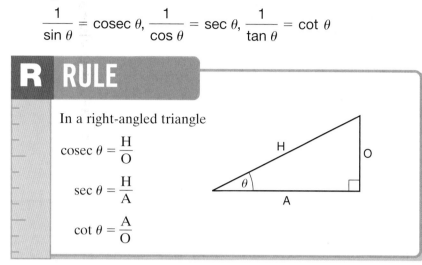

In a right-angled triangle

$$\operatorname{cosec} \theta = \frac{H}{O}$$

$$\sec \theta = \frac{H}{A}$$

$$\cot \theta = \frac{A}{O}$$

The graphs of the reciprocal functions are shown in the **Key facts** but there are several important points to note:

- The graphs of all three functions are periodic, with period 360° for $\operatorname{cosec} \theta$ and $\sec \theta$ and with period 180° for $\cot \theta$.
- Each of the graphs has asymptotes at intervals of 180° (when $\sin \theta = 0$, $\cos \theta = 0$, $\tan \theta = 0$).
- Both $y = \operatorname{cosec} \theta$ and $y = \sec \theta$ have the same range of $y \leqslant -1$ and $y \geqslant 1$.
- $y = \cot \theta$ can take any value.

✓ EXAMPLE 1

Find $\sec 210°$, leaving your answer in surd form.

SOLUTION

$$\sec 210° = \frac{1}{\cos 210°}$$

$$= \frac{1}{(-\cos 30°)}$$

$$= 1 \div \left(-\frac{\sqrt{3}}{2}\right)$$

$$= -\frac{2}{\sqrt{3}}$$

> Notice that $\cos 210° = -\cos 30°$.

✓ EXAMPLE 2

Solve the equation $\operatorname{cosec} x = -2.5$ for $0° \leqslant x \leqslant 360°$.

SOLUTION

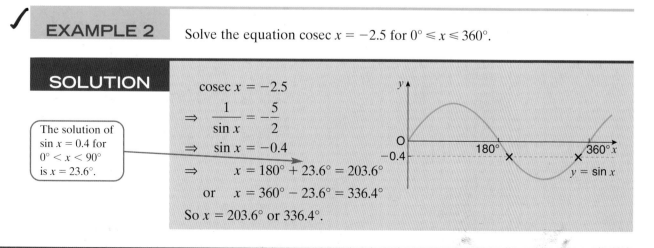

$$\operatorname{cosec} x = -2.5$$

$$\Rightarrow \quad \frac{1}{\sin x} = -\frac{5}{2}$$

$$\Rightarrow \quad \sin x = -0.4$$

$$\Rightarrow \quad x = 180° + 23.6° = 203.6°$$

$$\text{or} \quad x = 360° - 23.6° = 336.4°$$

So $x = 203.6°$ or $336.4°$.

> The solution of $\sin x = 0.4$ for $0° < x < 90°$ is $x = 23.6°$.

In C2 you met the identity $\sin^2 \theta + \cos^2 \theta = 1$ (which is Pythagoras' theorem written in trigonometry).

If you divide both sides of this identity by $\sin^2 \theta$ you get

$$\frac{\sin^2 \theta}{\sin^2 \theta} + \frac{\cos^2 \theta}{\sin^2 \theta} = \frac{1}{\sin^2 \theta}$$

As $\dfrac{\cos \theta}{\sin \theta} = \cot \theta$ and $\dfrac{1}{\sin \theta} = \operatorname{cosec} \theta$.

$$\Rightarrow \quad 1 + \cot^2 \theta = \operatorname{cosec}^2 \theta$$

Another important identity, proved in a similar way, is $\tan^2 \theta + 1 = \sec^2 \theta$.

✓ **EXAMPLE 3**   Solve the equation $\operatorname{cosec}^2 x = \cot x + 3$ for $0° \leq x \leq 360°$.

SOLUTION

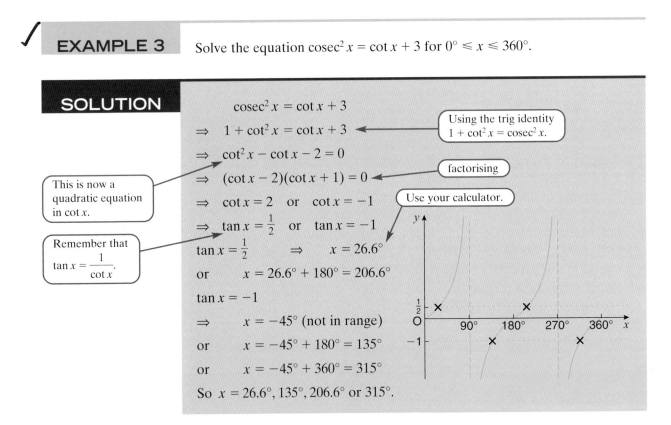

$$\operatorname{cosec}^2 x = \cot x + 3$$

$$\Rightarrow \quad 1 + \cot^2 x = \cot x + 3$$

Using the trig identity $1 + \cot^2 x = \operatorname{cosec}^2 x$.

$$\Rightarrow \quad \cot^2 x - \cot x - 2 = 0$$

$$\Rightarrow \quad (\cot x - 2)(\cot x + 1) = 0$$

factorising

This is now a quadratic equation in $\cot x$.

$$\Rightarrow \quad \cot x = 2 \quad \text{or} \quad \cot x = -1$$

Use your calculator.

$$\Rightarrow \quad \tan x = \tfrac{1}{2} \quad \text{or} \quad \tan x = -1$$

Remember that $\tan x = \dfrac{1}{\cot x}$.

$$\tan x = \tfrac{1}{2} \quad \Rightarrow \quad x = 26.6°$$

$$\text{or} \quad x = 26.6° + 180° = 206.6°$$

$$\tan x = -1$$

$$\Rightarrow \quad x = -45° \text{ (not in range)}$$

$$\text{or} \quad x = -45° + 180° = 135°$$

$$\text{or} \quad x = -45° + 360° = 315°$$

So $x = 26.6°, 135°, 206.6°$ or $315°$.

You should now be able to use cosec, sec and cot to prove further trig identities, as in Example 4.

✓ **EXAMPLE 4**   Show that $\dfrac{1}{1 - \cos \theta} + \dfrac{1}{1 + \cos \theta} = 2 \operatorname{cosec}^2 \theta$.

SOLUTION

The common denominator is $(1 - \cos \theta)(1 + \cos \theta)$

so $\dfrac{1}{1 - \cos \theta} + \dfrac{1}{1 + \cos \theta} = \dfrac{(1 + \cos \theta)}{(1 - \cos \theta)(1 + \cos \theta)} + \dfrac{(1 - \cos \theta)}{(1 - \cos \theta)(1 + \cos \theta)}$

$$= \frac{(1 + \cos \theta) + (1 - \cos \theta)}{(1 - \cos \theta)(1 + \cos \theta)}$$

$$= \frac{2}{1 - \cos^2 \theta}$$

$$= \frac{2}{\sin^2 \theta}$$

Using the trig identity $\sin^2 \theta + \cos^2 \theta = 1$.

As $\dfrac{1}{\sin \theta} = \operatorname{cosec} \theta$.

$$= 2 \operatorname{cosec}^2 \theta, \text{ as required.}$$

LINKS

The results and techniques of trigonometry are frequently used in many areas of mathematics.
A few examples are:
Mechanics   Projectiles (M1), Forces (M1–4) and Stability (M4).
Calculus   Differentiation, Integration and for substitutions used in evaluating integrals (C3 and FP2).
Geometry   Polar Co-ordinates (FP2) and Differential Geometry (FP3).

Test Yourself ⊃L

1 Find the exact value of $\operatorname{cosec} 240°$.

  A -2 B $-\dfrac{2}{\sqrt{3}}$ C $\dfrac{2}{\sqrt{3}}$ D $-\dfrac{\sqrt{3}}{2}$ E -1.155 (to 3 d.p.)

2 What is the solution of the equation $\tan^2 \theta = \sec \theta + 5$ in the range $0 \leqslant \theta \leqslant 2\pi$?

  A $1.23, 2.09$ B $70.5°, 120°, 240°, 289.5°$

  C $1.17, 2.27, 4.02, 5.11$ D $1.23, 2.09, 4.19, 5.05$

3 Three of the following statements are false and one is true. Which one is true?

  A $\sec \theta$, $\operatorname{cosec} \theta$ and $\cot \theta$ all have the same sign for $0 < \theta < \pi$.

  B As $1 + \cot^2 \theta = \operatorname{cosec}^2 \theta$ then $\operatorname{cosec} \theta > \cot \theta$.

  C $f(\theta) = \sec \theta$ is an even function.

  D The equation $\operatorname{cosec} \theta = \cot \theta$ has one root in the range $-180° \leqslant \theta \leqslant 180°$.

4 Three of the following identities are false and one is true. Which one is true?

  A $\sec^2 \theta + \operatorname{cosec}^2 \theta = 1$ B $\dfrac{\operatorname{cosec} \theta}{\sec \theta} = \tan \theta$

  C $\sec \theta \times \cot \theta = \operatorname{cosec} \theta$ D $(\cot \theta + 1)(\cot \theta - 1) = \operatorname{cosec}^2 \theta$

Exam-Style Question ⊃L

i)   Explain why the expression $\dfrac{4\operatorname{cosec} \theta - 2}{3\operatorname{cosec} \theta + 2}$ is not defined for $\theta = 0°, 180°$ or $360°$.

The function $f(\theta) = \dfrac{4\operatorname{cosec} \theta - 2}{3\operatorname{cosec} \theta + 2}$. Its domain is $0° < \theta < 360°$, $\theta \neq 180°$.

ii)   (A) Solve the equation $f(\theta) = 1$.   (B) Show that the equation $f(\theta) = -1$ has no solution.

iii) Show that, where it is defined, $f(\theta)$ can be written as $\dfrac{4 - 2\sin \theta}{3 + 2\sin \theta}$.

      Hence verify that $f(\theta)$ can also be written as $-1 + \dfrac{7}{3 + 2\sin \theta}$.

iv) The graph shows the curve $y = -1 + \dfrac{7}{3 + 2\sin \theta}$

      for $0° < \theta < 360°$.

      P is the lowest point and Q is the highest point.

      Find the co-ordinates of P and Q.

      Hence write down the range of $f(\theta)$.

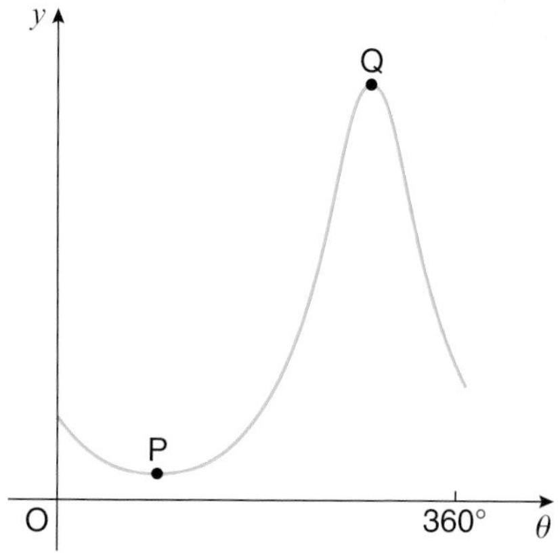

Compound-angle formulae

A **ABOUT THIS TOPIC**

This section introduces the compound-angle formulae for sin, cos and tan of the angles $(\theta + \phi)$ and $(\theta - \phi)$ and, as a special case, the double-angle formulae. There are several ways of proving these formulae; while you will find these interesting, you will not be asked to reproduce them in the C4 examination.

R **REMEMBER**

- The three main trigonometric (trig) functions, their graphs and the solution of trig equations from C2.
- The trig identity $\sin^2 \theta + \cos^2 \theta = 1$, from C2.
- Knowledge of sin, cos and tan of 30°, 45° and 60° from C2.

K **KEY FACTS**

Compound-angle formulae

- $\sin(\theta + \phi) = \sin \theta \cos \phi + \cos \theta \sin \phi$
- $\sin(\theta - \phi) = \sin \theta \cos \phi - \cos \theta \sin \phi$
- $\cos(\theta + \phi) = \cos \theta \cos \phi - \sin \theta \sin \phi$
- $\cos(\theta - \phi) = \cos \theta \cos \phi + \sin \theta \sin \phi$
- $\tan(\theta + \phi) = \dfrac{\tan \theta + \tan \phi}{1 - \tan \theta \tan \phi}$ $\quad (\theta + \phi) \neq 90°, 270°, \dots$
- $\tan(\theta - \phi) = \dfrac{\tan \theta - \tan \phi}{1 + \tan \theta \tan \phi}$ $\quad (\theta - \phi) \neq 90°, 270°, \dots$

Double-angle formulae

- $\sin 2\theta = 2 \sin \theta \cos \theta$
- $\cos 2\theta = \cos^2 \theta - \sin^2 \theta = 1 - 2 \sin^2 \theta = 2 \cos^2 \theta - 1$
- $\tan 2\theta = \dfrac{2 \tan \theta}{1 - \tan^2 \theta}$ $\quad \theta \neq 45°, 135°, \dots$
- $\sin^2 \theta = \frac{1}{2}(1 - \cos 2\theta)$
- $\cos^2 \theta = \frac{1}{2}(1 + \cos 2\theta)$

Using the compound-angle formulae

There are several ways in which you will be expected to use the compound-angle formulae and these are illustrated in the examples in this section.

- In the first two examples you are given the trigonometrical ratios for certain angles and asked to find the exact values of the trigonometrical ratios of related angles.
- A very useful application of the compound-angle formulae is in the double-angle formulae, as is shown in Example 3.
- Example 4 illustrates how you can use the compound-angle formulae and the double-angle formulae to solve equations.

✓ **EXAMPLE 1** Use the compound-angle formulae to calculate the **exact** value of cos 105°.

SOLUTION

$\cos 105° = \cos (60° + 45°)$ (Notice the word 'exact' – don't use your calculator.)

Using the compound-angle formula
$\cos(\theta + \phi) = \cos\theta \cos\phi - \sin\theta \sin\phi$ with $\theta = 60°$ and $\phi = 45°$

$\cos 105° = \cos 60° \cos 45° - \sin 60° \sin 45°$

$\cos 105° = \dfrac{1}{2} \times \dfrac{1}{\sqrt{2}} - \dfrac{\sqrt{3}}{2} \times \dfrac{1}{\sqrt{2}}$

$= \dfrac{1 - \sqrt{3}}{2\sqrt{2}}$

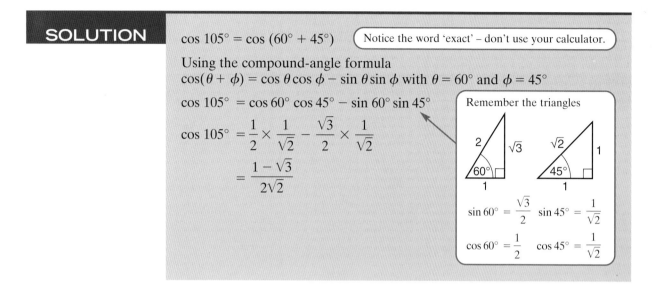

Remember the triangles

$\sin 60° = \dfrac{\sqrt{3}}{2}$ $\sin 45° = \dfrac{1}{\sqrt{2}}$

$\cos 60° = \dfrac{1}{2}$ $\cos 45° = \dfrac{1}{\sqrt{2}}$

✓ **EXAMPLE 2** You are given that $\sin x = \frac{15}{17}$ and $\cos y = \frac{3}{5}$, where x and y are both acute angles. Find the exact values of **i)** $\sin (x - y)$ and **ii)** $\tan (x + y)$.

SOLUTION

Start by finding the values of $\cos x$ and $\tan x$.

(Remember that you have been told that x is an acute angle and that $\sin x = \frac{15}{17}$.)

Using $\sin^2 x + \cos^2 x = 1$, $\left(\frac{15}{17}\right)^2 + \cos^2 x = 1$,

$\Rightarrow \quad \cos^2 x = 1 - \dfrac{225}{289} = \dfrac{64}{289}$

$\Rightarrow \quad \cos x = \pm\dfrac{8}{17}$

As x is an acute angle, $\cos x = +\frac{8}{17}$ and $\tan x = \frac{15}{8}$.

Similarly, using $\sin^2 y + \cos^2 y = 1$,

$\sin^2 y + \left(\frac{3}{5}\right)^2 = 1$, so $\sin^2 y = \frac{16}{25}$ and thus $\sin y = \pm\frac{4}{5}$.

As y is also an acute angle, $\sin y = +\frac{4}{5}$ and $\tan y = \frac{4}{3}$.

i) $\sin (x - y) = \sin x \cos y - \cos x \sin y$

$= \dfrac{15}{17} \times \dfrac{3}{5} - \dfrac{8}{17} \times \dfrac{4}{5}$

$= \dfrac{45 - 32}{85} = \dfrac{13}{85}$

ii) $\tan (x + y) = \dfrac{\tan x + \tan y}{1 - \tan x \tan y}$

$= \dfrac{\dfrac{15}{8} + \dfrac{4}{3}}{1 - \dfrac{15}{8} \times \dfrac{4}{3}}$

$= \dfrac{\dfrac{77}{24}}{-\dfrac{36}{24}} = -\dfrac{77}{36}$

The next example is about double-angle formulae.

EXAMPLE 3

i) By writing $\phi = \theta$, show that $\cos 2\theta = \cos^2 \theta - \sin^2 \theta$.

ii) Hence show that $\cos 2\theta = 2\cos^2 \theta - 1$ and $\cos 2\theta = 1 - 2\sin^2 \theta$.

SOLUTION

i) $\cos(\theta + \phi) = \cos\theta\cos\phi - \sin\theta\sin\phi$

Writing $\phi = \theta$ gives

$$\cos(\theta + \theta) = \cos\theta\cos\theta - \sin\theta\sin\theta$$

and so $\cos 2\theta = \cos^2 \theta - \sin^2 \theta$

ii) Since $\sin^2 \theta + \cos^2 \theta = 1$, $\sin^2 \theta = 1 - \cos^2 \theta$ and $\cos^2 \theta = 1 - \sin^2 \theta$.

So $\cos 2\theta = \cos^2 \theta - \sin^2 \theta$	$\cos 2\theta = \cos^2 \theta - \sin^2 \theta$
$\cos 2\theta = \cos^2 \theta - (1 - \cos^2 \theta)$	$\cos 2\theta = 1 - \sin^2 \theta - \sin^2 \theta$
$\cos 2\theta = 2\cos^2 \theta - 1$	$\cos 2\theta = 1 - 2\sin^2 \theta$

A ADVICE

Notice that there are three common ways of writing $\cos 2\theta$.

$$\cos 2\theta = \cos^2 \theta - \sin^2 \theta = 2\cos^2 \theta - 1 = 1 - 2\sin^2 \theta$$

A ADVICE

To show that $\sin 2\theta = 2\sin\theta\cos\theta$, substitute $\phi = \theta$ in the formula

$$\sin(\theta + \phi) = \sin\theta\cos\phi + \cos\theta\sin\phi$$

Similarly, substituting $\phi = \theta$ in $\tan(\theta + \phi) = \dfrac{\tan\theta + \tan\phi}{1 - \tan\theta\tan\phi}$ gives $\tan 2\theta = \dfrac{2\tan\theta}{1 - \tan^2 \theta}$.

The next example is about solving equations.

EXAMPLE 4

Solve the following equations for values of x in the range $0° \leqslant x \leqslant 360°$.

a) $\sin(x - 30°) = \cos(x + 45°)$

b) $3\sin 2x = \cos x$

c) $\tan 3x \tan x = 1$

SOLUTION

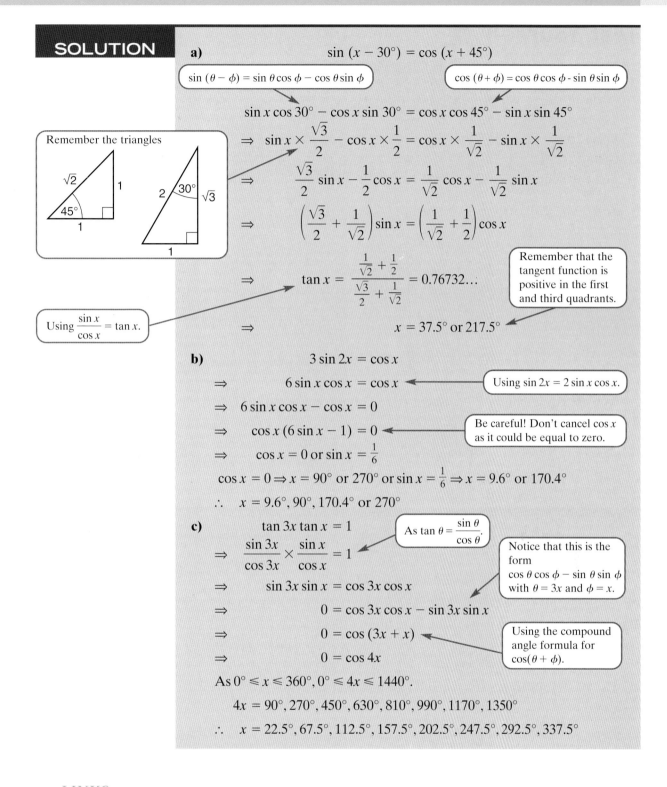

a)

$$\sin(x - 30°) = \cos(x + 45°)$$

$\sin(\theta - \phi) = \sin\theta\cos\phi - \cos\theta\sin\phi$

$\cos(\theta + \phi) = \cos\theta\cos\phi - \sin\theta\sin\phi$

$$\sin x \cos 30° - \cos x \sin 30° = \cos x \cos 45° - \sin x \sin 45°$$

$$\Rightarrow \quad \sin x \times \frac{\sqrt{3}}{2} - \cos x \times \frac{1}{2} = \cos x \times \frac{1}{\sqrt{2}} - \sin x \times \frac{1}{\sqrt{2}}$$

$$\Rightarrow \quad \frac{\sqrt{3}}{2}\sin x - \frac{1}{2}\cos x = \frac{1}{\sqrt{2}}\cos x - \frac{1}{\sqrt{2}}\sin x$$

$$\Rightarrow \quad \left(\frac{\sqrt{3}}{2} + \frac{1}{\sqrt{2}}\right)\sin x = \left(\frac{1}{\sqrt{2}} + \frac{1}{2}\right)\cos x$$

Remember the triangles

Using $\dfrac{\sin x}{\cos x} = \tan x.$

$$\Rightarrow \quad \tan x = \frac{\frac{1}{\sqrt{2}} + \frac{1}{2}}{\frac{\sqrt{3}}{2} + \frac{1}{\sqrt{2}}} = 0.76732\ldots$$

Remember that the tangent function is positive in the first and third quadrants.

$$\Rightarrow \quad x = 37.5° \text{ or } 217.5°$$

b)

$$3\sin 2x = \cos x$$

$$\Rightarrow \quad 6\sin x \cos x = \cos x$$

Using $\sin 2x = 2\sin x \cos x.$

$$\Rightarrow \quad 6\sin x \cos x - \cos x = 0$$

$$\Rightarrow \quad \cos x(6\sin x - 1) = 0$$

Be careful! Don't cancel $\cos x$ as it could be equal to zero.

$$\Rightarrow \quad \cos x = 0 \text{ or } \sin x = \frac{1}{6}$$

$$\cos x = 0 \Rightarrow x = 90° \text{ or } 270° \text{ or } \sin x = \frac{1}{6} \Rightarrow x = 9.6° \text{ or } 170.4°$$

$$\therefore \quad x = 9.6°, 90°, 170.4° \text{ or } 270°$$

c)

$$\tan 3x \tan x = 1$$

As $\tan\theta = \dfrac{\sin\theta}{\cos\theta}.$

$$\Rightarrow \quad \frac{\sin 3x}{\cos 3x} \times \frac{\sin x}{\cos x} = 1$$

$$\Rightarrow \quad \sin 3x \sin x = \cos 3x \cos x$$

Notice that this is the form $\cos\theta\cos\phi - \sin\theta\sin\phi$ with $\theta = 3x$ and $\phi = x$.

$$\Rightarrow \quad 0 = \cos 3x \cos x - \sin 3x \sin x$$

$$\Rightarrow \quad 0 = \cos(3x + x)$$

Using the compound angle formula for $\cos(\theta + \phi)$.

$$\Rightarrow \quad 0 = \cos 4x$$

As $0° \leqslant x \leqslant 360°, 0° \leqslant 4x \leqslant 1440°.$

$$4x = 90°, 270°, 450°, 630°, 810°, 990°, 1170°, 1350°$$

$$\therefore \quad x = 22.5°, 67.5°, 112.5°, 157.5°, 202.5°, 247.5°, 292.5°, 337.5°$$

LINKS

The results and techniques of trigonometry are frequently used in many areas of mathematics. A few examples are:

Mechanics   Projectiles (M1), Oscillations (M3 and M4), Stability (M4).
Calculus   Substitutions used in evaluating integrals (FP2).
Geometry   Polar Co-ordinates (FP2), Differential Geometry (FP3).

Test Yourself

1 You are given that $\tan\theta = \frac{24}{7}$ and θ is an acute angle. Find the values of $\sin 2\theta$ and $\cos 2\theta$.

A $\sin 2\theta = \frac{48}{25}$, $\cos 2\theta = \frac{14}{25}$

B $\sin 2\theta = \frac{336}{625}$, $\cos 2\theta = -\frac{527}{625}$

C $\sin 2\theta = -\frac{527}{625}$, $\cos 2\theta = \frac{336}{625}$

D $\sin 2\theta = \frac{336}{625}$, $\cos 2\theta = \frac{289}{625}$

2 Solve the equation $\cos 2\theta = \cos\theta - 1$ for $0 \leqslant \theta \leqslant 2\pi$.

A $60°, 90°, 270°, 300°$

B $\frac{\pi}{3}, \frac{\pi}{2}$

C $\frac{\pi}{3}, \frac{5\pi}{3}$

D $\frac{\pi}{3}, \frac{\pi}{2}, \frac{3\pi}{2}, \frac{5\pi}{3}$

3 Three of the following statements are false and one is true. Which one is true?

A $\dfrac{1 - \cos 2\theta}{\sin 2\theta} = \tan\theta$

B $\cos(A + B) - \cos(A - B) = 2\sin A \sin B$

C $\sin 3x = 3 \sin x \cos x$

D $\tan\left(\theta + \dfrac{\pi}{4}\right) = \tan\theta + 1$

4 You are given that $\sin P = \frac{3}{5}$, where P is an obtuse angle and $\cos Q = \frac{5}{13}$, where Q is an acute angle. Find the exact value of $\cos(P - Q)$.

A $-\dfrac{56}{65}$

B $-\dfrac{77}{65}$

C $\dfrac{16}{65}$

D $\dfrac{56}{65}$

Exam-Style Question

i) Find $\int x \cos(kx)\,dx$ where k is a non-zero constant.

ii) Starting with the standard formula for $\cos(\theta + \phi)$, show that $\cos^2 x = \dfrac{1}{2}(\cos 2x + 1)$.

iii) Use the results from parts i) and ii) to find $\int x \cos^2 x\,dx$.

iv) Show that $\cos(A + B) + \cos(A - B) = 2\cos A \cos B$. Hence show that $2\cos 3x \cos x = \cos 4x + \cos 2x$.

v) Use the results from parts i) and iv) to show that $\displaystyle\int_0^{\frac{\pi}{4}} 2x \cos 3x \cos x\,dx = \dfrac{(\pi - 3)}{8}$.

The forms $r\cos(\theta \pm \alpha)$, $r\sin(\theta \pm \alpha)$

A ABOUT THIS TOPIC

This section shows you how to write a function of the form $a\cos\theta \pm b\sin\theta$ as a single sine or cosine expression $r\cos(\theta \pm \alpha)$ or $r\sin(\theta \pm \alpha)$. Written like this it is easy to use them to sketch the graph of the function, find the maximum and minimum values and to solve equations. This is particularly helpful for work on oscillations.

R REMEMBER

- The three main trigonometric (trig) functions, their graphs and the solution of trig equations, from C2.
- The trig identity $\sin^2\theta + \cos^2\theta = 1$, from C2.
- Transformations of graphs from C3.
- The compound-angle formulae from C4.

K KEY FACTS

The r, α formulae

- $a\sin\theta + b\cos\theta = r\sin(\theta + \alpha)$
- $a\sin\theta - b\cos\theta = r\sin(\theta - \alpha)$
- $a\cos\theta + b\sin\theta = r\cos(\theta - \alpha)$
- $a\cos\theta - b\sin\theta = r\cos(\theta + \alpha)$

where $r = \sqrt{a^2 + b^2}$, $\cos\alpha = \dfrac{a}{r}$ and $\sin\alpha = \dfrac{b}{r}$.

The key technique required in this section is the ability to write expressions like $a\sin\theta + b\cos\theta$ as single sine or cosine functions. To do this you use one of the compound-angle formulae.

For example, to make $a\sin\theta + b\cos\theta$, where $a > 0$ and $b > 0$, into $r\sin(\theta + \alpha)$, where $0° < \alpha < 90°$, start by writing down the compound-angle formula $\sin(\theta + \alpha) = \sin\theta\cos\alpha + \cos\theta\sin\alpha$ and drawing this right-angled triangle.

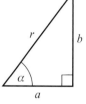

so $\qquad\qquad r = \sqrt{a^2 + b^2}$ (Using Pythagoras' theorem.)

and $\qquad\qquad \sin\alpha = \dfrac{b}{\sqrt{a^2 + b^2}}$, $\cos\alpha = \dfrac{a}{\sqrt{a^2 + b^2}}$

So $a\sin\theta + b\cos\theta = \sqrt{a^2 + b^2}\left(\sin\theta \times \dfrac{a}{\sqrt{a^2 + b^2}} + \cos\theta \times \dfrac{b}{\sqrt{a^2 + b^2}}\right)$

$\qquad\qquad\qquad\qquad = r(\sin\theta\cos\alpha + \cos\theta\sin\alpha)$

$\qquad\qquad\qquad\qquad = r\sin(\theta + \alpha)$

The first two examples here show you how to use this technique in particular cases.

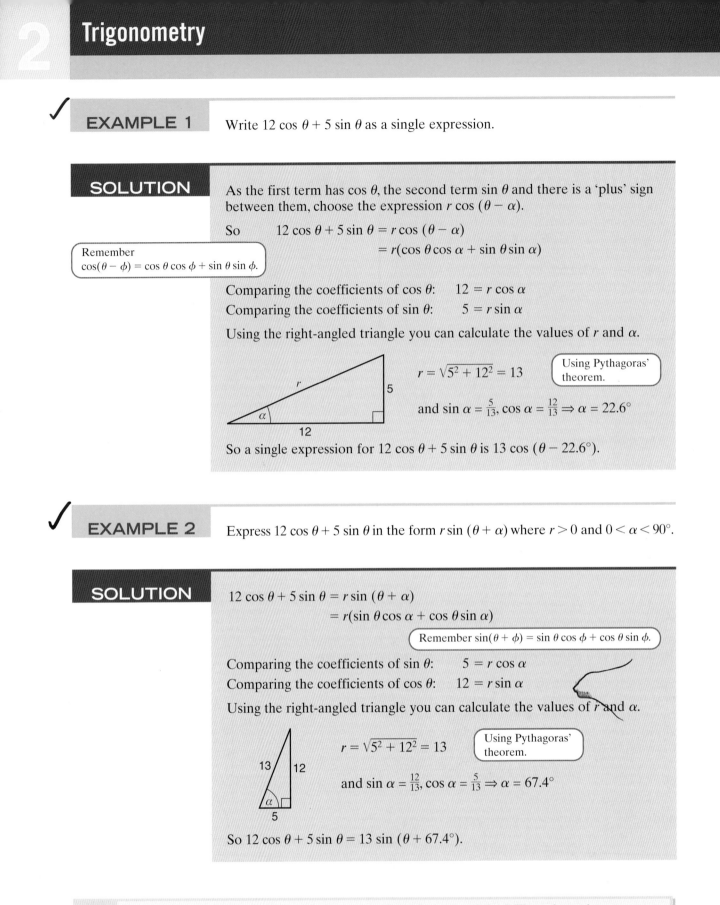

✓ **EXAMPLE 1**   Write $12 \cos \theta + 5 \sin \theta$ as a single expression.

SOLUTION   As the first term has $\cos \theta$, the second term $\sin \theta$ and there is a 'plus' sign between them, choose the expression $r \cos (\theta - \alpha)$.

So $12 \cos \theta + 5 \sin \theta = r \cos (\theta - \alpha)$
                            $= r(\cos \theta \cos \alpha + \sin \theta \sin \alpha)$

> **Remember**
> $\cos(\theta - \phi) = \cos \theta \cos \phi + \sin \theta \sin \phi$.

Comparing the coefficients of $\cos \theta$: $12 = r \cos \alpha$
Comparing the coefficients of $\sin \theta$: $5 = r \sin \alpha$

Using the right-angled triangle you can calculate the values of r and α.

$r = \sqrt{5^2 + 12^2} = 13$

> Using Pythagoras' theorem.

and $\sin \alpha = \frac{5}{13}$, $\cos \alpha = \frac{12}{13} \Rightarrow \alpha = 22.6°$

So a single expression for $12 \cos \theta + 5 \sin \theta$ is $13 \cos (\theta - 22.6°)$.

✓ **EXAMPLE 2**   Express $12 \cos \theta + 5 \sin \theta$ in the form $r \sin (\theta + \alpha)$ where $r > 0$ and $0 < \alpha < 90°$.

SOLUTION $12 \cos \theta + 5 \sin \theta = r \sin (\theta + \alpha)$
                            $= r(\sin \theta \cos \alpha + \cos \theta \sin \alpha)$

> Remember $\sin(\theta + \phi) = \sin \theta \cos \phi + \cos \theta \sin \phi$.

Comparing the coefficients of $\sin \theta$: $5 = r \cos \alpha$
Comparing the coefficients of $\cos \theta$: $12 = r \sin \alpha$

Using the right-angled triangle you can calculate the values of r and α.

$r = \sqrt{5^2 + 12^2} = 13$

> Using Pythagoras' theorem.

and $\sin \alpha = \frac{12}{13}$, $\cos \alpha = \frac{5}{13} \Rightarrow \alpha = 67.4°$

So $12 \cos \theta + 5 \sin \theta = 13 \sin (\theta + 67.4°)$.

⚠ Examples 1 and 2 both start with the expression $12 \cos \theta + 5 \sin \theta$. They show that an expression of the form $a \cos \theta \pm b \sin \theta$ can be written in the form $r \cos (\theta \pm \alpha)$ or $r \sin (\theta \pm \alpha)$ in more than one way. There is no single correct answer.

The next example shows you how you can go on to use an expression in this form.

✓ **EXAMPLE 3**

i) Express $\sin\theta - \cos\theta$ in the form $r\sin(\theta - \alpha)$ where $r > 0$ and $0 < \alpha < \dfrac{\pi}{2}$.

ii) State the maximum and minimum values of $\sin\theta - \cos\theta$.

iii) Sketch the graph of $y = \sin\theta - \cos\theta$ for $0 \leqslant \theta \leqslant 2\pi$.

iv) Solve the equation $\sin\theta - \cos\theta = \dfrac{1}{\sqrt{2}}$ for $0 \leqslant \theta \leqslant 2\pi$.

SOLUTION

i) $\sin\theta - \cos\theta = r\sin(\theta - \alpha)$

Notice that this is $1\sin\theta - 1\cos\theta$.

$= r(\sin\theta\cos\alpha - \cos\theta\sin\alpha)$

> **Remember**
> $\sin(\theta - \phi)$
> $= \sin\theta\cos\phi - \cos\theta\sin\phi$.

Comparing the coefficients of $\sin\theta$: $1 = r\cos\alpha$

Comparing the coefficients of $\cos\theta$: $1 = r\sin\alpha$

The triangle shows you that $r = \sqrt{1^2 + 1^2} = \sqrt{2}$ and the angle $\alpha = 45°$.

However the question says that $0 < \alpha < \dfrac{\pi}{2}$. This is telling you that α is

in radians so $\alpha = \dfrac{\pi}{4}$ giving $\sin\theta - \cos\theta = \sqrt{2}\sin\left(\theta - \dfrac{\pi}{4}\right)$

ii) $\sin\theta - \cos\theta = \sqrt{2}\sin\left(\theta - \dfrac{\pi}{4}\right)$

As the sine function oscillates between 1 and -1,

$\sqrt{2}\sin\left(\theta - \dfrac{\pi}{4}\right)$ will oscillate between $\sqrt{2}$ and $-\sqrt{2}$.

So the maximum value of $\sin\theta - \cos\theta$ is $\sqrt{2}$

and the minimum value of $\sin\theta - \cos\theta$ is $-\sqrt{2}$.

iii)

The graph of $y = \sqrt{2}\sin\left(\theta - \dfrac{\pi}{4}\right)$ in the range $0 \leqslant \theta \leqslant 2\pi$ can be

obtained from the graph of $y = \sin\theta$ by a translation of $\begin{pmatrix} \frac{\pi}{4} \\ 0 \end{pmatrix}$ and a

one-way stretch, scale factor $\sqrt{2}$, parallel to the y axis.

iv)

$$\sin\theta - \cos\theta = \frac{1}{\sqrt{2}}$$

$$\therefore \quad \sqrt{2}\sin\left(\theta - \frac{\pi}{4}\right) = \frac{1}{\sqrt{2}}$$

$$\therefore \quad \sin\left(\theta - \frac{\pi}{4}\right) = \frac{1}{2}$$

> $\sin 30° = \frac{1}{2}$, $30° = \frac{\pi}{6}$ radians
>
> $\sin 150° = \frac{1}{2}$, $150° = \frac{5\pi}{6}$ radians

$$\therefore \quad \left(\theta - \frac{\pi}{4}\right) = \frac{\pi}{6} \text{ or } \frac{5\pi}{6}$$

$$\therefore \quad \theta = \frac{5\pi}{12} \text{ or } \frac{13\pi}{12}$$

So the roots of the equation $\sin\theta - \cos\theta = \frac{1}{\sqrt{2}}$ in the range $0 \leqslant \theta \leqslant 2\pi$ are $\frac{5\pi}{12}$ and $\frac{13\pi}{12}$.

LINKS

The results and techniques of trigonometry are frequently used in many areas of mathematics. A few examples are:

Mechanics   Simple Harmonic Motion (M3).
Differential Equations   Oscillations.

Test Yourself ▷L

1 What are the values of r and α when $4\cos\theta + 3\sin\theta$ is expressed in the form $r\cos(\theta - \alpha)$, where $r > 0$ and $0 < \alpha < \frac{\pi}{2}$?

A $r = 5$, $\alpha = 53.1°$ B $r = 5$, $\alpha = 0.644$ C $r = 25$, $\alpha = 0.644$ D $r = 5$, $\alpha = 36.9°$

2 Solve the equation $3\sin 2\theta + 5\cos 2\theta = 4$ in the range $0° \leqslant \theta \leqslant 180°$.
Give your answers correct to 1 decimal place.

A $38.8°$, $172.1°$ B $77.6°$ C $38.8°$ D $6.2°$, $52.9°$

3 Find the maximum and minimum points of the function $f(\theta) = \sqrt{3}\cos\theta + \sin\theta$ in the range $0 < \theta < 2\pi$.

A $\min\left(\frac{\pi}{6}, 2\right)$, $\max\left(\frac{7\pi}{6}, -2\right)$ B $\min(210°, -2)$, $\max(30°, 2)$

C $\min\left(\frac{7\pi}{6}, -2\right)$, $\max\left(\frac{\pi}{6}, 2\right)$ D $\min\left(\frac{4\pi}{3}, -2\right)$, $\max\left(\frac{\pi}{3}, 2\right)$

4 The graph of $y = \frac{3\sqrt{3}}{2}\cos x - \frac{3}{2}\sin x$ can be obtained from the graph of $y = \cos x$ by a translation and a stretch. Describe the translation and the stretch.

A Translation $\begin{pmatrix} -\frac{\pi}{6} \\ 0 \end{pmatrix}$ and one-way stretch, scale factor $\frac{1}{3}$, parallel to the x axis

B Translation $\begin{pmatrix} \frac{\pi}{6} \\ 0 \end{pmatrix}$ and one-way stretch, scale factor 3, parallel to the y axis

C Translation $\begin{pmatrix} \frac{\pi}{6} \\ 0 \end{pmatrix}$ and one-way stretch, scale factor $\frac{1}{3}$, parallel to the x axis

D Translation $\begin{pmatrix} -\frac{\pi}{6} \\ 0 \end{pmatrix}$ and one-way stretch, scale factor 3, parallel to the y axis

Exam-Style Question ⊃L

The two parallel lines AB and CD are d cm apart. PQRS is a rectangle with P on AB and R on CD. PQ = 12 cm, QR = 5 cm and $\angle$BPQ = θ. BQD is a straight line at right angles to the two parallel lines.

i)   Show that $d = 12 \sin \theta + 5 \cos \theta$.

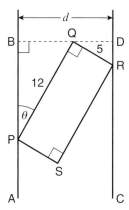

ii) Express $12 \sin \theta + 5 \cos \theta$ in the form $r \sin(\theta + \alpha)$, where $r > 0$ and $0° < \alpha < 90°$.

iii) Sketch the curve with equation $y = 12 \sin \theta + 5 \cos \theta$ for $0° \leqslant \theta \leqslant 360°$.
     Mark on your sketch the co-ordinates of
     (A) the points where the curve meets the axes
     (B) the maximum and minimum points.

iv) (A) Find the distance between the parallel lines when the angle θ is 30°.
     (B) Find the value of the acute angle θ when the lines are 10 cm apart.

Parametric equations 3

Introduction to parametric equations

A — ABOUT THIS TOPIC

Until now you have considered equations of lines and curves given in the form $y = f(x)$. However, in some cases, these equations are complicated and some curves just cannot be written in this way. It is sometimes easier to write the x and y co-ordinates in terms of some intermediate variable called a parameter.

R — REMEMBER

- Curve sketching from C1–3.
- Co-ordinate geometry from C1.
- Trigonometric identities from C2.

- The equation of a curve is often written in cartesian form, for example $y = \frac{3}{4}x^2$.

- A curve may also be written in parametric form. Thus the curve $y = \frac{3}{4}x^2$ is the same as $x = 2t$, $y = 3t^2$, where t is a parameter.

- The cartesian equation of the curve is obtained by eliminating the parameter between the two equations for x and y.

- When plotting a curve given in parametric form, the x and y co-ordinates of individual points lying on the curve can be found by substituting different values for the parameter into the two equations.

- The same information is required when sketching a curve given in parametric form as when sketching a curve given in cartesian form:
  a) the points of intersection with the axes
  b) any restrictions on the values that x and y can take
  c) the behaviour of the curve as x and y tend to ∞.

The first two examples show how to draw curves that are given by parametric equations and to describe their shapes.

✓ **EXAMPLE 1**   A curve is given by $x = 1 - t$, $y = t^2$.

   i)   Plot the curve for values of t between -3 and $+3$.

   ii)   Describe the symmetry of the curve.

SOLUTION

i)

t	−3	−2	−1	0	1	2	3
$x = 1 − t$	4	3	2	1	0	−1	−2
$y = t^2$	9	4	1	0	1	4	9

ii)

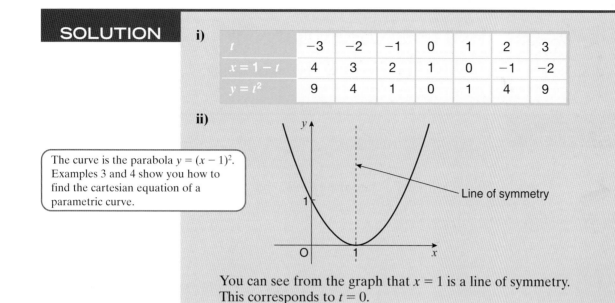

Line of symmetry

The curve is the parabola $y = (x − 1)^2$. Examples 3 and 4 show you how to find the cartesian equation of a parametric curve.

You can see from the graph that $x = 1$ is a line of symmetry. This corresponds to $t = 0$.

✔

EXAMPLE 2

A curve has parametric equations $x = t + 2, y = \dfrac{1}{t}$.

i) Find the co-ordinates of points on the curve for the following values of t: $-3, -2, -1, -0.5, 0.5, 1, 2, 3$.

ii) Are there any values of x for which the curve is undefined?

iii) Plot the points you have found and join them to give the curve.

SOLUTION

i)

t	−3	−2	−1	−0.5	0.5	1	2	3
$x = t + 2$	−1	0	1	1.5	2.5	3	4	5
$y = \dfrac{1}{t}$	$-\frac{1}{3}$	$-\frac{1}{2}$	−1	−2	2	1	$\frac{1}{2}$	$\frac{1}{3}$

ii) The curve is not defined when $t = 0$. Since $y = \dfrac{1}{t}$, y is undefined at that point.

When $t = 0$, $x = 2$ and this is the equation of an asymptote to the curve. The x axis is also an asymptote.

iii)

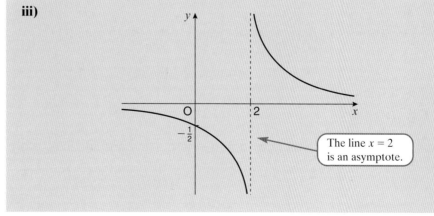

The line $x = 2$ is an asymptote.

You will often be asked to find the cartesian equation of a curve given in parametric form. You must eliminate the parameter between the two equations and the next two examples show you how to do this.

EXAMPLE 3

Find the cartesian equation of the curve with parametric equations

$$x = t + 2, y = \frac{1}{t-1}.$$

SOLUTION

Rearrange the expression for x to make t the subject.

$$x = t + 2 \Rightarrow t = x - 2$$

Now substitute this into the expression for y.

$$y = \frac{1}{(x-2) - 1}$$

$$y = \frac{1}{x - 3}$$

A ADVICE

Always use the co-ordinate with the linear equation
(if there is one) to get the substitution for the parameter.

EXAMPLE 4

Find the cartesian equation of the curve given by the parametric equations
$x = \cos \theta + \sin \theta, y = 2 \cos \theta + \sin \theta.$

SOLUTION

By subtracting the expressions for x and y obtain expressions for $\cos \theta$
and $\sin \theta$.

$$\begin{array}{ll} y = 2 \cos \theta + \sin \theta & 2x = 2 \cos \theta + 2 \sin \theta \\ x = \cos \theta + \sin \theta & y = 2 \cos \theta + \sin \theta \\ \hline y - x = \cos \theta & 2x - y = \sin \theta \end{array}$$

Remember
$(x - y)(x - y)$
$= x^2 - 2xy + y^2$.

Now use the identity $\sin^2 \theta + \cos^2 \theta = 1$

$$(2x - y)^2 + (y - x)^2 = 1$$

Expand the brackets $(4x^2 - 4xy + y^2) + (y^2 - 2xy + x^2) = 1$

Collect like terms $5x^2 - 6xy + 2y^2 = 1$

This is the cartesian equation.

The next example shows you how to find where a line and a curve given
parametrically intersect.

EXAMPLE 5

Find the co-ordinates of the points where the line $y = 2x$ cuts the curve
$x = t^2, y = t^3.$

To find the points of intersection, substitute $x = t^2$, $y = t^3$ into the equation of the line.

$$y = 2x$$
$$t^3 = 2t^2$$
$$t^3 - 2t^2 = 0$$
Factorising $\quad t^2(t - 2) = 0$
$$t = 0 \text{ or } 2$$

When $t = 0$, $x = 0$ and $y = 0$.

When $t = 2$, $x = 4$ and $y = 8$.

The points of intersection of the line and the curve are $(0, 0)$ and $(4, 8)$.

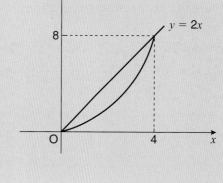

LINKS

Pure Mathematics Co-ordinate Geometry (FP1).

Mechanics Finding the path of a projectile (M1).

Test Yourself ▶L

1 Find the cartesian equation of the curve given by the parametric equations $x = 2t^2$, $y = 4(t - 1)$.

A $y = \pm\sqrt{8x - 16}$

B $y = -4 \pm \sqrt{8x}$

C $y = -4 \pm \sqrt{2x}$

D $y = -1 \pm \sqrt{8x}$

2 Find the cartesian equation of the curve given by the parametric equations $x = \cos\theta - \sin\theta$, $y = \sin\theta + 2\cos\theta$.

A $5x^2 - 2xy + 2y^2 = 9$

B $37x^2 - 34xy + 10y^2 = 9$

C $-3x^2 - 2xy + 2y^2 = 9$

D $5x^2 - 2xy + 2y^2 = 3$

3 A curve is defined parametrically by $x = 3 + 5\cos\theta$, $y = 5\sin\theta - 2$. Three of the following statements are false and one is true. Which statement is true?

A The curve is a circle centre $(3, 2)$ and radius 5.

B The curve cuts the y axis at the point where $\theta = 0.41$ radians.

C There is only one point on the curve with x co-ordinate 3.

D At the point $(8, -2)$, $\theta = 0$.

4 A line has equation $y = 2x + 3$ and a curve has equations $x = 3t$, $y = \dfrac{3}{t}$.

Three of the following statements are false and one is true. Which statement is true?

A The line and curve intersect at points $(-3, -3)$ and $(1\frac{1}{2}, 6)$.

B The line and curve intersect at $(-3, -3)$ and $(1\frac{1}{2}, 1\frac{1}{2})$.

C The line and curve intersect at $(3, 3)$ only.

D The line and curve do not intersect at any point.

Exam-Style Question ▷L

A curve C has parametric equations $x = 2t^2$, $y = 4t$. A line p passes through the point $(2, 0)$ and has gradient $\frac{4}{3}$.

i) Find the equation of line p.

ii) Find the values of the parameter t for which p intersects C and hence write down the co-ordinates of the point(s) of intersection.

A second line q has equation $3y = 4x + 12$.

iii) Prove that the line q does not intersect the curve C.

iv) From the equations of p and q what can you deduce about the lines?

v) Work out the cartesian equation of C and draw a sketch showing C, p and q on the same set of axes.

Parametric differentiation

A ABOUT THIS TOPIC

You will often need to find the gradient of a curve that is given parametrically. The technique for doing this is covered in this section.

R REMEMBER

- Basic differentiation from C2.
- The chain rule from C3.
- Differentiation of trigonometric functions from C3.
- Stationary points from C2.
- Co-ordinate geometry from C1.
- Curve sketching from C1–3.

K KEY FACTS

- When a curve is defined by parametric equations, with parameter t,

$$\frac{dy}{dx} = \frac{\dfrac{dy}{dt}}{\dfrac{dx}{dt}}.$$

The standard result for differentiation of parametric equations

You met the chain rule in C3, that is $\dfrac{dy}{dx} = \dfrac{dy}{dt} \times \dfrac{dt}{dx}$.

You also met the result that $\dfrac{dx}{dy} = \dfrac{1}{\dfrac{dy}{dx}}$ or, in this case $\dfrac{dt}{dx} = \dfrac{1}{\dfrac{dx}{dt}}$.

Putting these two results together gives you $\dfrac{dy}{dx} = \dfrac{\dfrac{dy}{dt}}{\dfrac{dx}{dt}}$.

This is the standard result you use to differentiate parametric equations. The first example shows you how to use it.

✓

EXAMPLE 1

A curve has parametric equations $x = 4t^2 + 5$, $y = 2t$.

Find $\dfrac{dy}{dx}$ in terms of the parameter t.

SOLUTION

Differentiating

$$y = 2t \Rightarrow \frac{dy}{dt} = 2$$

$$x = 4t^2 + 5 \Rightarrow \frac{dx}{dt} = 8t$$

$$\frac{dy}{dx} = \frac{\dfrac{dy}{dt}}{\dfrac{dx}{dt}}$$

Therefore

$$\frac{dy}{dx} = \frac{2}{8t} = \frac{1}{4t}$$

In long examination questions you are often asked to use the gradient function, $\dfrac{dy}{dx}$, to find the equation of tangents and normals at points on parametric curves, and to find stationary points. The next two examples are typical.

EXAMPLE 2

A curve has parametric equations $x = 2 \sin t$, $y = \cos 2t$.

i) Find the co-ordinates of the points where $t = -\dfrac{\pi}{2}, -\dfrac{\pi}{6}, 0, \dfrac{\pi}{6}, \dfrac{\pi}{2}$.

Draw the curve for $-\dfrac{\pi}{2} \leqslant t \leqslant \dfrac{\pi}{2}$, using equal scales for x and y.

ii) Show that $\dfrac{dy}{dx} = -2 \sin t$.

iii) Find the equation of the tangents and normals at the points where $t = -\dfrac{\pi}{6}$ and $\dfrac{\pi}{6}$.

iv) Add these tangents and normals to your graph. What shape is formed by the four lines?

SOLUTION

i)

t	$-\dfrac{\pi}{2}$	$-\dfrac{\pi}{6}$	0	$\dfrac{\pi}{6}$	$\dfrac{\pi}{2}$
$(x, y) = (2 \sin t, \cos 2t)$	$(-2, -1)$	$(-1, \frac{1}{2})$	$(0, 1)$	$(1, \frac{1}{2})$	$(2, -1)$

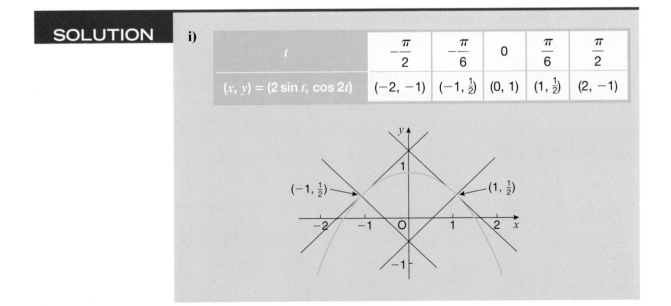

ii) $x = 2 \sin t \Rightarrow \dfrac{dx}{dt} = 2 \cos t$

$y = \cos 2t \Rightarrow \dfrac{dy}{dt} = -2 \sin 2t$

$\dfrac{dy}{dx} = \dfrac{\dfrac{dy}{dt}}{\dfrac{dx}{dt}}$

> Remember
> $\sin 2t = 2 \sin t \cos t.$

$\Rightarrow \dfrac{dy}{dx} = \dfrac{-2 \sin 2t}{2 \cos t} = \dfrac{-4 \sin t \cos t}{2 \cos t}$

$\Rightarrow \dfrac{dy}{dx} = -2 \sin t$ as required

> For perpendicular lines
> $m_1 m_2 = -1, m_2 = -\dfrac{1}{m_1}.$

iii) When $t = -\dfrac{\pi}{6}$, $(x, y) = (-1, \tfrac{1}{2})$, $\dfrac{dy}{dx} = -2 \times -\tfrac{1}{2} = +1$

Gradients: tangent at $(-1, \tfrac{1}{2})$ is 1, normal is $-\dfrac{1}{1} = -1$

Equations: tangent $y - \tfrac{1}{2} = 1(x - (-1))$ normal $y - \tfrac{1}{2} = -1(x - (-1))$

> Using
> $y - y_1 = m(x - x_1).$

$\qquad\qquad\qquad y = x + \tfrac{3}{2} \qquad\qquad\qquad y = -x - \tfrac{1}{2}$

When $t = \dfrac{\pi}{6}$, $(x, y) = (1, \tfrac{1}{2})$, $\dfrac{dy}{dx} = -2 \times \tfrac{1}{2} = -1$

Gradients: tangent at $(1, \tfrac{1}{2})$ is -1, normal is $-\dfrac{1}{-1} = 1$

Equations: tangent $y - \tfrac{1}{2} = -1(x - 1)$ normal $y - \tfrac{1}{2} = 1(x - 1)$

$\qquad\qquad\qquad y = -x + \tfrac{3}{2} \qquad\qquad\qquad y = x - \tfrac{1}{2}$

iv) The four lines form a square, as can be seen from the diagram.

✓ **EXAMPLE 3**

The graph shows the curve with parametric equations $x = 4 - t^2$, $y = 4t - 3t^3$.

i) Find the values of t at the points where the curve crosses the axes. Hence find the co-ordinates of these points.

ii) Find $\dfrac{dy}{dx}$ in terms of t and hence find the co-ordinates of the turning points.

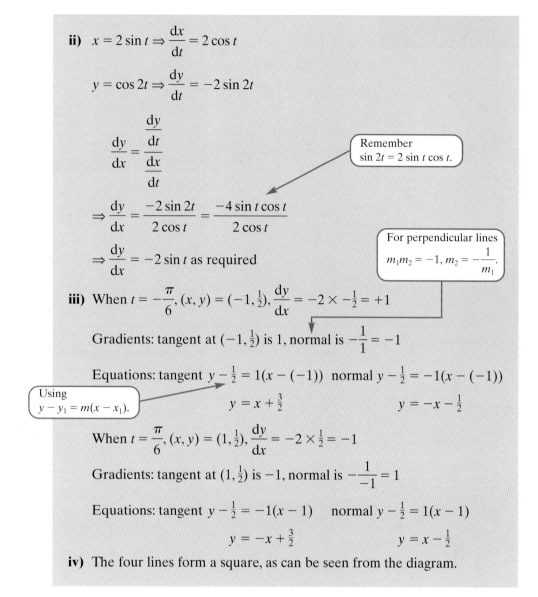

i) When the curve crosses the y axis, $x = 0$.

$$4 - t^2 = 0 \quad \Rightarrow \quad t^2 = 4$$
$$t = 2 \text{ or } t = -2$$

When $t = 2$, $y = 4 \times 2 - 3 \times 2^3 = 8 - 24 = -16$.
The point is $(0, -16)$.
When $t = -2$,
$y = 4 \times -2 - 3 \times (-2^3) = -8 - 3 \times (-8) = -8 + 24 = +16$.
The point is $(0, 16)$.

The curve cuts the y axis at the points $(0, -16)$ and $(0, 16)$.

When the curve cuts the x axis, $y = 0$

$$4t - 3t^3 = 0$$
$$\Rightarrow \quad t(4 - 3t^2) = 0$$
$$\Rightarrow \quad 3t(t^2 - \tfrac{4}{3}) = 0$$
$$t = 0, +\sqrt{\tfrac{4}{3}} \text{ or } -\sqrt{\tfrac{4}{3}}$$

When $t = 0$, $x = 4 - 0^2 = 4$ so the point is $(4, 0)$.

When $t = \sqrt{\tfrac{4}{3}}$, $x = 4 - \tfrac{4}{3} = \tfrac{8}{3}$ so the point is $(\tfrac{8}{3}, 0)$.

When $t = -\sqrt{\tfrac{4}{3}}$, $x = 4 - \tfrac{4}{3} = \tfrac{8}{3}$ so the point is $(\tfrac{8}{3}, 0)$.

The curve crosses the x axis at $(4, 0)$ and twice at $(\tfrac{8}{3}, 0)$.

ii) $x = 4 - t^2 \quad \Rightarrow \quad \dfrac{dx}{dt} = -2t$

$y = 4t - 3t^3 \quad \Rightarrow \quad \dfrac{dy}{dt} = 4 - 9t^2$

$$\frac{dy}{dx} = \frac{\dfrac{dy}{dt}}{\dfrac{dx}{dt}}$$

$$\Rightarrow \quad \frac{dy}{dx} = \frac{4 - 9t^2}{-2t}$$

$\dfrac{dy}{dx} = 0$ when

$$\frac{4 - 9t^2}{-2t} = 0$$
$$\Rightarrow 9t^2 = 4$$
$$\Rightarrow t = \pm\sqrt{\tfrac{4}{9}} = \pm\tfrac{2}{3}$$

When $t = \tfrac{2}{3}$, $x = 4 - \tfrac{4}{9} = 3\tfrac{5}{9}$, $y = \tfrac{8}{3} - \tfrac{8}{9} = \tfrac{16}{9} = 1\tfrac{7}{9}$ so the point is $(3\tfrac{5}{9}, 1\tfrac{7}{9})$.

When $t = -\tfrac{2}{3}$, $x = 3\tfrac{5}{9}$, $y = -\tfrac{16}{9} = -1\tfrac{7}{9}$ so the point is $(3\tfrac{5}{9}, -1\tfrac{7}{9})$.

LINKS

Differential Equations   Simultaneous Differential Equations (DE).
Mechanics   Projectiles (M1), Resisted Motion (M4).

Test Yourself ▷L

1 A curve has parametric equations $x = 4t$, $y = 1 - \dfrac{1}{t}$. Find the value of $\dfrac{dy}{dx}$ when $t = 3$.

  A $\dfrac{1}{36}$ B 36   C $\dfrac{4}{9}$ D $-\dfrac{1}{36}$

2 Find the gradient of the curve given parametrically by $x = 2\cos^3 t$, $y = 2\sin^3 t$.

  A $\tan t$ B $-\cot^3 t$ C $-\tan t$ D $-\tan^2 t$

3 A curve is given by $x = t^2 + 1$, $y = t(t-3)^2$. Three of the following statements are false and one is true. Which statement is true?

  A The curve has no stationary points.

  B The curve has one stationary point only at $(10, 0)$.

  C The curve has stationary points at $(10, 0)$ and $(2, 4)$.

  D The curve has stationary points at $(1, 0)$ and $(10, 0)$.

4 The parametric equations of a curve are given by $x = \cos 2t$, $y = 4\sin t$. At the point where $t = \dfrac{\pi}{2}$, three of the following statements are false and one is true. Which statement is true?

  A The equation of the normal at the point where $t = \dfrac{\pi}{2}$ is $y = x + 3$.

  B The equation of the tangent at the point where $t = \dfrac{\pi}{2}$ is $x + y = 3$.

  C When $t = 0$, $\dfrac{dy}{dx} = 0$.

  D The x axis and the y axis are both normals to the curve.

Exam-Style Question ▷L

The graph shows the curve with parametric equations $x = 2t$, $y = \dfrac{2}{t}$.

P and Q are points on the same branch of the curve, with parameters p and q respectively.

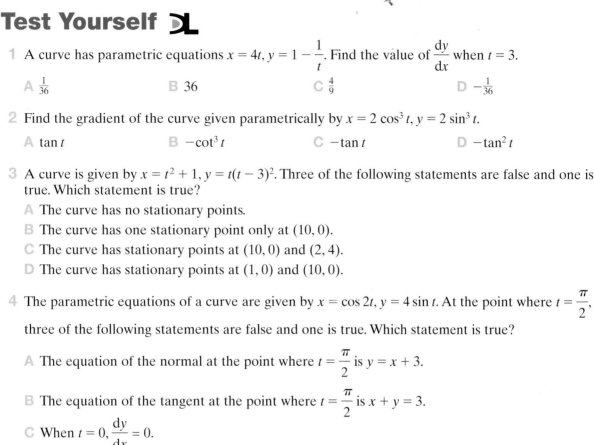

i) Find the gradient of the chord PQ.
Hence find the equation of the chord PQ.

ii) Explain why replacing q by p in the equation of the chord gives the equation of the tangent at P. Show that this is $y = -\dfrac{1}{p^2}x + \dfrac{4}{p}$.

iii) Find $\dfrac{dy}{dx}$ for the curve in terms of t.

iv) Verify that when $t = p$, $\dfrac{dy}{dx}$ is the same as the gradient of the equation that you derived in part ii).

v) Tangents from two points on the curve pass through the point $(3, 1)$. Find the co-ordinates of the points of contact with the curve.

Further techniques for integration

▶▶ 254
261

Volumes of revolution

A ABOUT THIS TOPIC

You have studied the use of integration to find the **area** of a region 'under a graph'. In this section integration is applied to the problem of finding the **volume** of a solid with rotational symmetry about a line, where the solid is generated by rotating a region of a plane about the x or y axes.

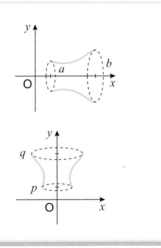

R REMEMBER

- Curve sketching from C1, C2 and C3.
- Techniques of integration from C2, C3 and C4.
- The use of integration to find an area from C2.

K KEY FACTS

- About the x axis, the volume of revolution is $\int_a^b \pi y^2 \, \mathrm{d}x$.

- About the y axis, the volume of revolution is $\int_p^q \pi x^2 \, \mathrm{d}y$.

A ADVICE

The process used in this topic is known informally as 'finding a volume of revolution'. Many examples in your book and almost all examination questions describe the process of rotating 'a region of a plane through 360° (or 2π radians)' about the x or y axes. The volume of the solid so formed is what is called the 'volume of revolution'.

A ADVICE

The formulae have a factor of π and it is usual to leave this as a factor of your answer unless you have been asked for a numerical answer. Similarly, your answers may contain surds and these should be left as they are unless you have been asked for a numerical answer. You may well have answers such as 21π or $10\sqrt{5}\pi$.

In some problems the unit of length is not given and so the volume can only be said to be in units of volume or 'cubic units'.

Solids formed by rotation about the x axis

The simplest case is when the region has the x axis as one of its edges.

EXAMPLE 1

i) Draw a sketch of the curve $y = \frac{1}{8}x^3 + 1$ and shade the region R bounded by the curve, the lines $x = 1$ and $x = 2$, and the x axis.

ii) Find the volume of the solid formed when R is rotated through $360°$ about the x axis.

SOLUTION

i)

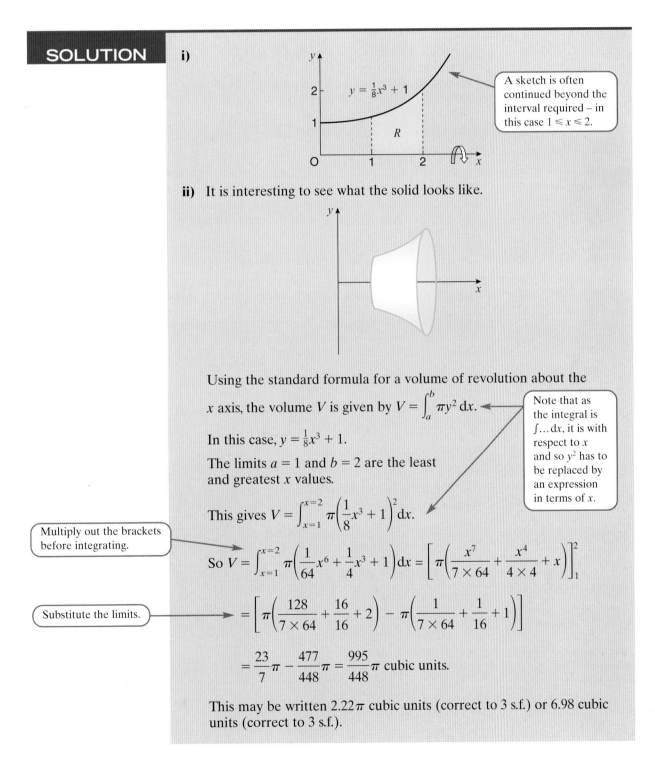

A sketch is often continued beyond the interval required – in this case $1 \leqslant x \leqslant 2$.

ii) It is interesting to see what the solid looks like.

Using the standard formula for a volume of revolution about the x axis, the volume V is given by $V = \int_a^b \pi y^2 \, dx.$

Note that as the integral is $\int \ldots dx$, it is with respect to x and so y^2 has to be replaced by an expression in terms of x.

In this case, $y = \frac{1}{8}x^3 + 1$.

The limits $a = 1$ and $b = 2$ are the least and greatest x values.

This gives $V = \int_{x=1}^{x=2} \pi \left(\frac{1}{8}x^3 + 1\right)^2 dx.$

Multiply out the brackets before integrating.

So $V = \int_{x=1}^{x=2} \pi \left(\frac{1}{64}x^6 + \frac{1}{4}x^3 + 1\right) dx = \left[\pi \left(\frac{x^7}{7 \times 64} + \frac{x^4}{4 \times 4} + x\right)\right]_1^2$

Substitute the limits.

$= \left[\pi\left(\frac{128}{7 \times 64} + \frac{16}{16} + 2\right) - \pi\left(\frac{1}{7 \times 64} + \frac{1}{16} + 1\right)\right]$

$= \frac{23}{7}\pi - \frac{477}{448}\pi = \frac{995}{448}\pi$ cubic units.

This may be written 2.22π cubic units (correct to 3 s.f.) or 6.98 cubic units (correct to 3 s.f.).

A slightly more complicated situation arises when the region does not have the x axis as one boundary. A way of doing such problems that cuts down the work is shown in Example 2.

EXAMPLE 2

The region enclosed by the curves $y = 3 - x^2$ and $y = x^2 + 1$ is rotated through $360°$ about the x axis. Find the volume of the solid formed.

SOLUTION

Although you have not been asked to sketch the curves and the region, you will find it very hard to answer the question unless you do so.

You need the volume of revolution of the region shaded green. To find this you will need to find the volume of revolution of the region under the curve $y = 3 - x^2$ (shaded red and green) and subtract from it the volume of revolution of the region under the curve $y = x^2 + 1$ (shaded red).

Before you can do any of the integration, you have to find the least and greatest values of x in the regions being rotated. These are at the points where the curves cross and their x values are found by solving the equations of the curves simultaneously.

You have $\left. \begin{array}{l} y = 3 - x^2 \\ y = x^2 + 1 \end{array} \right\} \Rightarrow x^2 + 1 = 3 - x^2 \Rightarrow 2x^2 = 2.$

Hence $x^2 = 1$ and $x = \pm 1$ and each of the integrals is from -1 to 1.

Using the standard formula, the volume of revolution of the region under

$y = x^2 + 1$ is $\quad V_1 = \int_{x=-1}^{x=1} \pi(x^2 + 1)^2 \, dx = \int_{x=-1}^{x=1} \pi(x^4 + 2x^2 + 1) \, dx.$

The area under $y = 3 - x^2$ is

$$V_2 = \int_{x=-1}^{x=1} \pi(3 - x^2)^2 \, dx = \int_{x=-1}^{x=1} \pi(9 - 6x^2 + x^4) \, dx.$$

You need $V_2 - V_1$.

You could work out each of the integrals and then subtract the values, but it is often quicker to use the fact that the integrals are between the same limits and combine them. In this example

$$V_2 - V_1 = \int_{x=-1}^{x=1} \pi(9 - 6x^2 + x^4) \, dx - \int_{x=-1}^{x=1} \pi(x^4 + 2x^2 + 1) \, dx$$

$$= \int_{-1}^{1} [\pi(9 - 6x^2 + x^4) - \pi(x^4 + 2x^2 + 1)] \, dx$$

$$= \int_{-1}^{1} \pi(8 - 8x^2) \, dx = \left[\pi \left(8x - \frac{8x^3}{3} \right) \right]_{-1}^{1}$$

$$= \pi \left(8 - \frac{8}{3} \right) - \pi \left(8 \times (-1) - \frac{8 \times (-1)}{3} \right)$$

$$= \frac{16}{3} \pi - \left(-\frac{16}{3} \right) \pi$$

giving $\frac{32}{3} \pi$ cubic units.

The first two examples have had answers in 'cubic units'. In some situations you are given dimensions that enable you to express your answer in cm^3, m^3, etc. For instance, in Example 2 you might have been told that the final solid measured 6 cm along its axis of symmetry.

Using 'real' units will be discussed further in the Test Yourself Question 4 at the end of this section.

In the next example one boundary is a line parallel to the axis of rotation, giving a shape with a cylindrical hole through the middle.

EXAMPLE 3

i) Draw a sketch of the curve $y = 2e^{\frac{x}{3}}$ and shade the region R bounded by the curve, the line $x = 3$ and the line $y = 2$.

ii) Find the volume of the solid formed when R is rotated through $360°$ about the x axis.

SOLUTION

i) The region R is shaded green.

ii) To find the volume of revolution about the x axis of the green region, you need to find the volume of revolution of the region under the curve $y = 2e^{\frac{x}{3}}$ (shaded green and blue) and subtract from it the volume of the cylinder formed by rotating the line $y = 2$ (shaded blue).

Hence the volume required is

$$\int_{x=0}^{x=3} \pi \left(2e^{\frac{x}{3}}\right)^2 dx \textbf{ minus } \text{the volume of the cylinder.}$$

Using the formula $V = \pi r^2 h$ for the volume of the cylinder with $r = 2$ and $h = 3$, gives 12π cubic units.

The volume of revolution of the region under $y = 2e^{\frac{x}{3}}$ is

$$\int_{x=0}^{x=3} \pi \left(2e^{\frac{x}{3}}\right)^2 dx = \int_0^3 4\pi e^{\frac{2x}{3}} dx$$

$$= \left[4\pi \times \frac{e^{\frac{2x}{3}}}{\frac{2}{3}}\right]_0^3 = \left[4\pi \times \frac{3}{2} \times e^{\frac{2x}{3}}\right]_0^3$$

$$= 6\pi e^2 - 6\pi e^0 = 6\pi e^2 - 6\pi$$

Subtracting the volume of the cylinder gives $6\pi e^2 - 6\pi - 12\pi = 6\pi(e^2 - 3)$ cubic units.

Solids formed by rotation about the y axis

The principle is the same as for rotation about the x axis but in this case

the formula is $V = \int_p^q \pi x^2 \, dy$ so the integration is with respect to y and x^2

has to be expressed in terms of y; the values p and q refer to the least and greatest y values.

EXAMPLE 4

A region is enclosed by the curve $y = x^2 - 1$ from $x = 1$ to $x = 2$, the x axis, the y axis and the line $y = 3$. This region is rotated through $360°$ about the y axis. Find the volume of the solid formed.

SOLUTION

The region to be rotated is shaded green in the diagram.

The volume is $V = \int_p^q \pi x^2 \, dy$ and it is

easy to see that $p = 0$ and $q = 3$.

Rearranging gives $y = x^2 - 1$ which gives $x^2 = y + 1$ and so

$$V = \int_{y=0}^{y=3} \pi(y + 1) \, dy = \left[\pi\left(\frac{y^2}{2} + y\right) \right]_0^3$$

so $V = \left[\pi\left(\frac{3^2}{2} + 3\right) - \pi(0 - 0) \right] = \frac{15}{2}\pi$ cubic units.

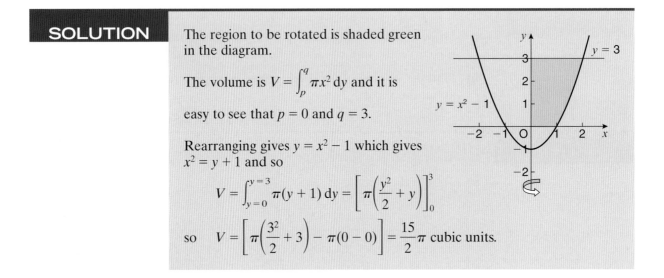

A ADVICE

Examples may require integration of trigonometric functions. As the standard integrals for these functions require the angle to be measured in radians, you may also be told that the rotation of a region about one of the axes is through 2π radians instead of $360°$.

LINKS

Pure Mathematics   Applications of Calculus (DE, FP2).
Mechanics   Applications of Calculus (M3, M4).

Test Yourself ▶L

1 Draw a sketch of the curve $y = 2x - x^2$ and shade the region R bounded by this curve, the x axis and the line $x = 1$. Calculate the volume of the solid formed when R is rotated by $360°$ about the x axis.

A $\frac{2}{3}\pi$ cubic units   B $\frac{8}{15}\pi$ cubic units

C $\frac{23}{15}\pi$ cubic units   D $\frac{1}{3}\pi$ cubic units

2 The region S is bounded by the curve $y = x^{\frac{3}{2}}$ from $x = 1$ to $x = 2$, the line $y = 1$ and the line $x = 2$. Calculate the volume of the solid formed when S is rotated by $360°$ about the x axis. The volume, correct to 3 significant figures, is

A 11.8 cubic units

B 2.75 cubic units

C 8.64 cubic units

D 9.17 cubic units

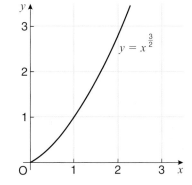

3 The diagram shows the graph of the curve $y^2 = 4x$ and the region T.

Calculate the volume of the solid formed when T is rotated through $360°$ about the y axis.

A 96.8π cubic units

B 160π cubic units

C 208π cubic units, correct to 3 s.f.

D 738π cubic units, correct to 3 s.f.

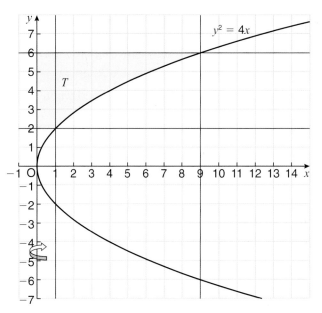

4 The region U shown in the diagram is bounded by the curve $y = \sqrt{2x - 2}$, the x axis and the line $x = k$. Find, in terms of k and π, an expression for the volume of the solid formed when U is rotated through $360°$ about the x axis. Also find the volume of this solid in the case when the plane circular face has a diameter of 8 cm.

A $\pi k(k - 2); 63\pi\,\text{cm}^3$

B $\pi(k^2 - 2k - 1); 62\pi\,\text{cm}^3$

C $\pi(k - 1)^2; 1024\pi\,\text{cm}^3$

D $\pi(k - 1)^2; 64\pi\,\text{cm}^3$

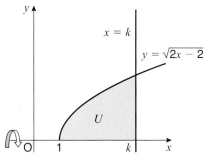

Exam-Style Question ⊃L

The graph shows part of the curve $y = \sqrt{2x^2 + 7}$. It passes through the points $(1, 3)$ and $(3, 5)$.

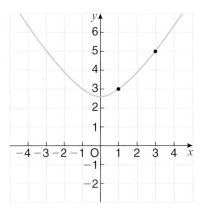

i) On a sketch, shade the region R bounded by: the x axis; the line $x = 1$; the line $x = 3$; the curve $y = \sqrt{2x^2 + 7}$ from $x = 1$ to $x = 3$.

ii) Find the volume of the solid formed when R is rotated through $360°$ about the x axis.

iii) On another sketch, shade the region S bounded by: the line $y = 3$; the line $x = 3$; the curve $y = \sqrt{2x^2 + 7}$ from $x = 1$ to $x = 3$.

iv) Find the volume of the solid formed when S is rotated through $360°$ about the y axis.

Integration

You have now met all the different methods that you need to know for integration in C4; this section will help you decide which of those methods to use.

Not all functions can be integrated by the techniques you have met so far (or indeed integrated at all), so you may need to use a numerical method to find the approximate value of a definite integral. You have already used the trapezium rule in C2; in C4, as well as using the rule, you need to be able to justify the accuracy of your answer.

R · REMEMBER

- Integration using partial fractions from C4.
- Natural logarithms from C3.
- Integration from C3.
- The trapezium rule from C2.

K · KEY FACTS

- The trapezium rule to find an approximate value of a definite integral is:

$$A \approx \tfrac{1}{2} \times h \times [y_0 + y_n + 2(y_1 + y_2 + \ldots + y_{n-1})]$$

where n is the number of strips and h is the strip width.

Increasing the number of strips will, in general, increase the accuracy of your answer.

The trapezium rule

Sometimes you will have a function which can't be integrated using any of the techniques you have learned. When this happens you can find an approximate value for the area under a curve using the trapezium rule. Note the trapezium rule is a numerical method and so can only be used for definite integrals.

Remember that the trapezium rule is

$$A \approx \tfrac{1}{2} \times h \times [y_0 + y_n + 2(y_1 + y_2 + \ldots + y_{n-1})]$$

where n is the number of strips and h is the strip width.

In general, the more strips that are used the more accurate the approximation is. In C4 you may be asked to find this area to a stated degree of accuracy – for example to 2 decimal places. You should apply the trapezium rule a few times with an increasing number of strips in order to see how quickly the answers are converging so you can justify a given degree of accuracy.

You can remember this as $\tfrac{1}{2}$ stripwidth × [first + last + 2 × middles].

In this case the trapezium rule gives an **underestimate**.

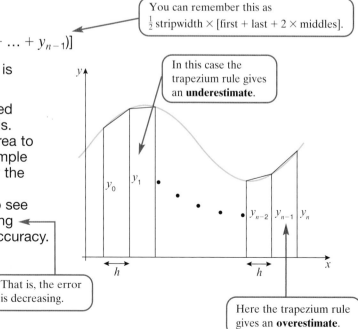

That is, the error is decreasing.

Here the trapezium rule gives an **overestimate**.

EXAMPLE 1

The diagram shows the graph of $y = \sin \sqrt{x}$.

The shaded area between the curve, the x axis and the lines $x = 1$ and $x = 2$ has been divided into 4 strips.

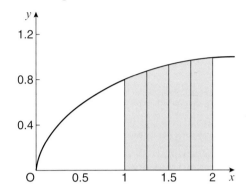

i) Use the trapezium rule with 4 strips to estimate the value of $\int_1^2 \sin \sqrt{x} \, dx$.

Write down the first 6 significant figures of the answer from your calculator display.
State with a reason whether your answer is an underestimate or an overestimate.

ii) Use the trapezium rule again with **A)** 8 strips and **B)** 16 strips to obtain an estimate for the value of $\int_1^2 \sin \sqrt{x} \, dx$.

iii) Comment on the accuracy to which you can give the integral.

SOLUTION

i) The trapezium rule is $A \approx \frac{1}{2} \times h \times [y_0 + y_n + 2(y_1 + y_2 + \ldots + y_{n-1})]$.

The strip width $h = \dfrac{2-1}{4} = 0.25.$ ← Divide the width of the whole interval by the number of strips.

$x_0 = 1$	$x_1 = 1.25$	$x_2 = 1.5$	$x_3 = 1.75$	$x_4 = 2$
$y_0 = \sin\sqrt{1} = \sin 1$	$y_1 = \sin\sqrt{1.25}$	$y_2 = \sin\sqrt{1.5}$	$y_3 = \sin\sqrt{1.75}$	$y_4 = \sin\sqrt{2}$

Now substitute into the trapezium rule:
$$A \approx \tfrac{1}{2} \times 0.25 \times [\sin 1 + \sin\sqrt{2} + 2(\sin\sqrt{1.25} + \sin\sqrt{1.5} + \sin\sqrt{1.75})]$$
$$\approx 0.931001\ldots$$

The trapezium rule gives an underestimate for the area as the trapezia all lie below the curve.

Using more strips will improve the approximation and so will give a slightly greater answer than 0.931001.

Don't forget to work out the new strip width!

ii) **A)** Using 8 strips gives the strip width $h = \dfrac{2-1}{8} = \dfrac{1}{8}.$

$x_0 = 1$	$x_1 = 1.125$	$x_2 = 1.25$	$x_3 = 1.375$	$x_4 = 1.5$
$y_0 = \sin 1$	$y_1 = \sin\sqrt{1.125}$	$y_2 = \sin\sqrt{1.25}$	$y_3 = \sin\sqrt{1.375}$	$y_4 = \sin\sqrt{1.5}$
$x_5 = 1.625$	$x_6 = 1.75$	$x_7 = 1.875$	$x_8 = 2$	
$y_5 = \sin\sqrt{1.625}$	$y_6 = \sin\sqrt{1.75}$	$y_7 = \sin\sqrt{1.875}$	$y_8 = \sin\sqrt{2}$	

Now substitute into the trapezium rule:

$$A \approx \tfrac{1}{2} \times \tfrac{1}{8} \times [\sin1 + \sin\sqrt{2} + 2(\sin\sqrt{1.125} + \sin\sqrt{1.25} + \sin\sqrt{1.375} + \sin\sqrt{1.5} + \sin\sqrt{1.625} + \sin\sqrt{1.75} + \sin\sqrt{1.875})]$$

$$\approx 0.931839...$$

B) Using 16 strips gives the strip width $h = \dfrac{2-1}{16} = \dfrac{1}{16}$.

When you substitute into the trapezium rule you get:

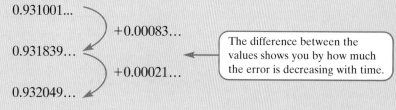

$$A \approx \tfrac{1}{2} \times \tfrac{1}{16} \times [\sin1 + \sin\sqrt{2} + 2(\sin\sqrt{1.0625} + ... + \sin\sqrt{1.9375})]$$

$$\approx 0.932049...$$

> In a non-exam situation you can use a spreadsheet to work this out!

iii) The 3 applications of the trapezium rule give:

0.931001...

$+0.00083...$

0.931839...

> The difference between the values shows you by how much the error is decreasing with time.

$+0.00021...$

0.932049...

You can confidently give the answer to 2 decimal places as the 3 applications of the trapezium rule seem to be converging to 0.93...

However, you can see from the way the error is decreasing that it seems likely that the integral is actually 0.932 to 3 d.p.

When should you use the trapezium rule? The answer is for a definite integral which you can't do any other way. On the next two pages there is a flow chart which will help you decide the best method for any integral you may meet in C4.

Integrals in C4

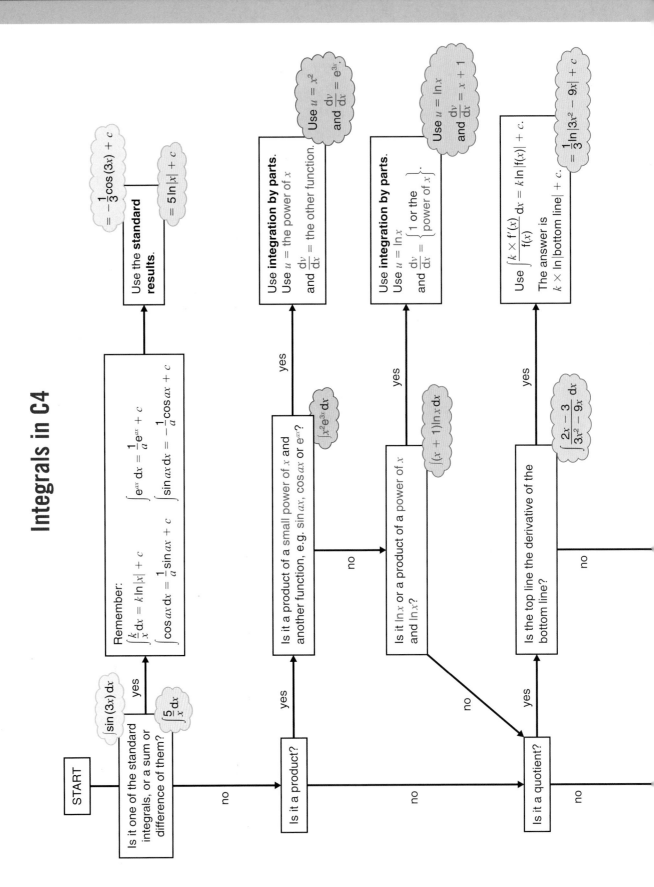

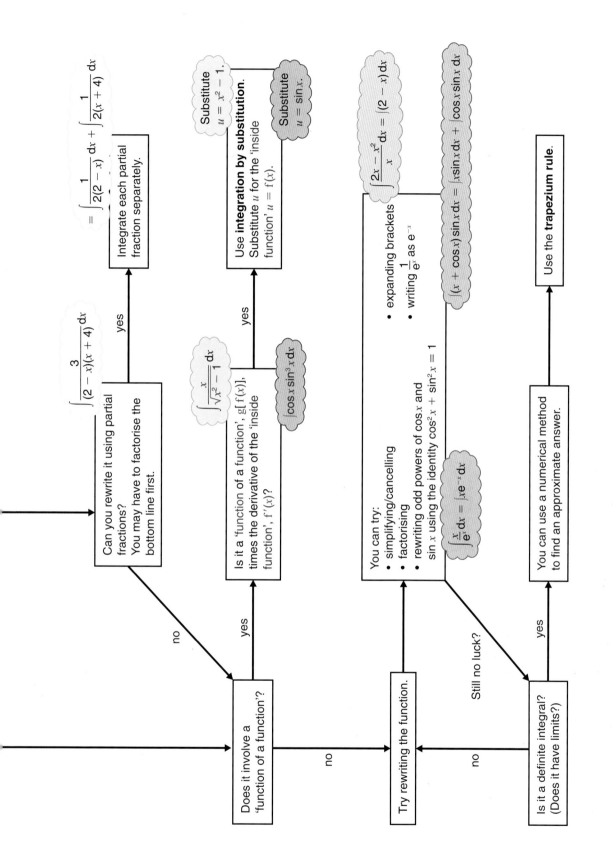

4 Further techniques for integration

Use the next example and the flow chart on pages 46–47 to help you decide which method to use for integration.

EXAMPLE 2   Use the flow chart on pages 46–47 to help you choose the right method to integrate each of these.

a) $\displaystyle\int_0^1 x e^{x^2}\,dx$ b) $\displaystyle\int_0^1 x e^{2x}\,dx$ c) $\displaystyle\int_0^1 e^{x^2}\,dx$

SOLUTION

a) e^{x^2} is a function of a function and the derivative of x^2 is $2x$ so the integral is in the form $f'(x) \times g[f(x)]$.
So you should use integration by substitution. Use the substitution $u = x^2$.

b) $x e^{2x}$ is a product of a small power of x and a standard function, e^{2x}, so you should use integration by parts.

c) At first glance it looks as though you can integrate e^{x^2} using one of the methods you met in C4. However, it is not a product so you can't use integration by parts, and although e^{x^2} is a function of a function the integral is not in the form $f'(x) \times g[f(x)]$ so you can't use substitution.

> You can't use integration by substitution because the derivative of $2x$ is not x.

$\displaystyle\int_0^1 e^{x^2}\,dx$ is a definite integral so you can use the trapezium rule to find an approximation for its value.

LINKS

Pure Mathematics	Calculus (FP2), Differential Geometry (FP3), Differential Equations (DE), Numerical Methods.
Mechanics	Volumes of Revolution and Centres of Mass (M3), Variable Force and Mass (M4), Moments of Inertia.
Statistics	Probability Density Functions (S3), Variance.

Test Yourself ⊃L

In questions 1–3, when you have found the right method use it to find the integral.

1 Which method should you use to integrate $\int (6x + 1)\sqrt{(9x^2 + 3x)}\,dx$?

   A Integration using the substitution $u = 6x + 1$

   B Integration using the substitution $u = 9x^2 + 3x$

   C Integration by parts

   D The trapezium rule

2 Which method should you use to integrate $\int_1^2 x^3 \ln x\,dx$?

   A Integration using the substitution $u = x^3$

   B Integration by parts using $u = x^3$ and $\dfrac{dv}{dx} = \ln x$

   C Integration by parts using $u = \ln x$ and $\dfrac{dv}{dx} = x^3$

   D The trapezium rule

3 Which method should you use to integrate $\int_2^3 \dfrac{x}{x^2 + 1}\,dx$?

There are two correct answers. Check you can find both of them.

A Integration using the substitution $u = x^2 + 1$

B Integration using partial fractions

C Integration using the rule $\int \dfrac{k \times f'(x)}{f(x)}\,dx = k\ln|f(x)| + c$

D Integration by parts

E The trapezium rule

4 Use repeated applications of the trapezium rule to estimate the value of $\int_0^\pi \sqrt{2 - \cos^2 x}\,dx$ correct to 2 decimal places.

A 15.28　　　　　B 2.30　　　　　C 3.82　　　　　D 4.11

5 The diagram opposite shows the graph of $y = f(x)$.

Three of the following statements are false and one is true. Which statement is true?

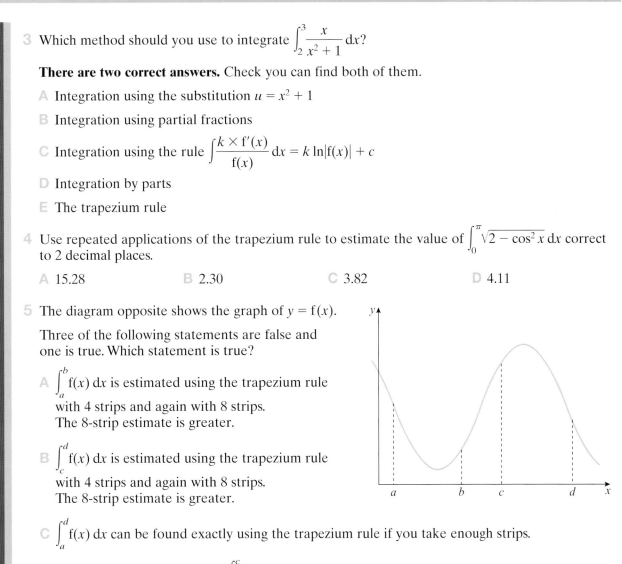

A $\displaystyle\int_a^b f(x)\,dx$ is estimated using the trapezium rule with 4 strips and again with 8 strips. The 8-strip estimate is greater.

B $\displaystyle\int_c^d f(x)\,dx$ is estimated using the trapezium rule with 4 strips and again with 8 strips. The 8-strip estimate is greater.

C $\displaystyle\int_a^d f(x)\,dx$ can be found exactly using the trapezium rule if you take enough strips.

D Using the trapezium rule for $\displaystyle\int_a^c f(x)\,dx$ gives an underestimate.

Exam-Style Question ⊃L

i) Use the trapezium rule with **A**) 2 strips and **B**) 4 strips to obtain an approximation for $\int_1^2 \dfrac{12}{1 + x^2}\,dx$.

In each case, write down the first 6 figures from your calculator display.

ii) By comparing your two answers to part i), state with a reason whether the trapezium rule is likely to be an underestimate or an overestimate for the value of the integral.

The trapezium rule with 8 strips gives 3.86632...
The trapezium rule with 16 strips gives 3.86233...

iii) Show that the error decreases with each application of the trapezium rule.

iv) Without applying the trapezium rule again, give the value of $\int_1^2 \dfrac{12}{1 + x^2}\,dx$ to as many decimal places as you can justify.

Vectors

5

275
289, 299
315

Introduction to vectors

A ABOUT THIS TOPIC

Vectors are important in many areas of mathematics. In this section you look at the basic ideas about vectors in two and three dimensions.

R REMEMBER

- Pythagoras' theorem from GCSE.
- Co-ordinate geometry from C1.

K KEY FACTS

- A **scalar** quantity has **magnitude** only.
- A **vector** quantity has both **magnitude** and **direction**.
- Two vectors are **equal** if they have the same magnitude and the same direction.
- Two vectors are **parallel** if they have the same direction.
- A **unit vector** is a vector with magnitude 1.
- The unit vectors in the x, y and z direction are denoted as $\mathbf{i}$, $\mathbf{j}$ and $\mathbf{k}$ respectively.
- The **position vector** of a point P is the vector from the origin, O, to P. This is written as $\overrightarrow{OP}$ or $\mathbf{p}$. If P has co-ordinates (a, b, c) then the position vector of P can be written as $a\mathbf{i} + b\mathbf{j} + c\mathbf{k}$ or as a **column vector** $\begin{pmatrix} a \\ b \\ c \end{pmatrix}$.
- The **magnitude** of a vector is found using Pythagoras' theorem. The vector $a\mathbf{i} + b\mathbf{j} + c\mathbf{k}$ has magnitude $\sqrt{a^2 + b^2 + c^2}$.

Describing vectors

A vector in two dimensions is often represented by a straight line with an arrowhead, which shows the direction of the vector. The direction is usually taken to be the angle that the vector makes with the positive x axis, measured in an anticlockwise direction. The length of the line represents the magnitude of the vector.

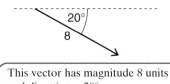

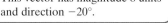

This vector has magnitude 8 units and direction $-20°$.

Vectors can also be described using components in the x and y directions.

The unit vector (a vector of length 1) in the x direction is denoted by $\mathbf{i}$, and the unit vector in the y direction is denoted by $\mathbf{j}$. Vectors can also be written as column vectors.

Vectors are printed in bold, for example $\mathbf{a}$.

In handwriting vectors are underlined, for example $\underline{a}$.

The vector from point A to point B is written as $\overrightarrow{AB}$.

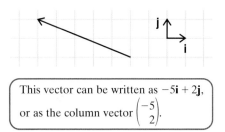

This vector can be written as $-5\mathbf{i} + 2\mathbf{j}$, or as the column vector $\begin{pmatrix} -5 \\ 2 \end{pmatrix}$.

Calculating with vectors

When a vector is multiplied by a scalar (a number), then each component is multiplied by the scalar.

Two vectors in component form can be added or subtracted by dealing with each component separately.

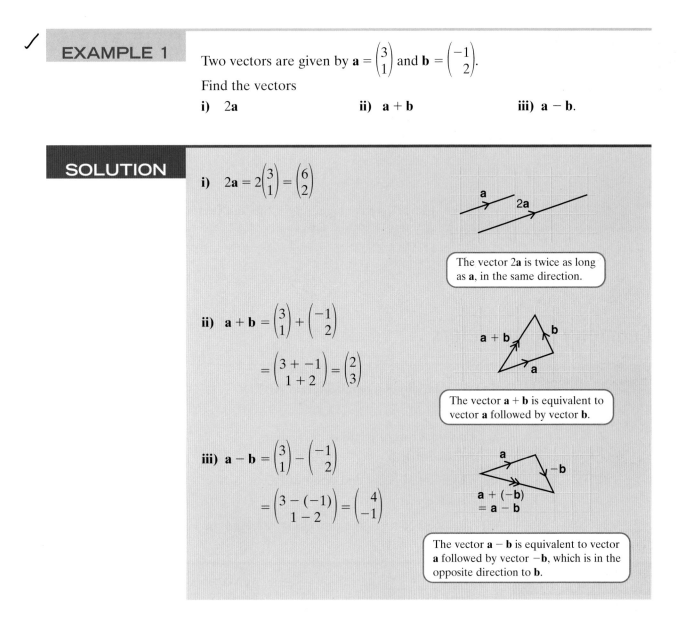

EXAMPLE 1

Two vectors are given by $\mathbf{a} = \begin{pmatrix} 3 \\ 1 \end{pmatrix}$ and $\mathbf{b} = \begin{pmatrix} -1 \\ 2 \end{pmatrix}$.

Find the vectors

i) $2\mathbf{a}$ ii) $\mathbf{a} + \mathbf{b}$ iii) $\mathbf{a} - \mathbf{b}$.

SOLUTION

i) $2\mathbf{a} = 2\begin{pmatrix} 3 \\ 1 \end{pmatrix} = \begin{pmatrix} 6 \\ 2 \end{pmatrix}$

The vector $2\mathbf{a}$ is twice as long as $\mathbf{a}$, in the same direction.

ii) $\mathbf{a} + \mathbf{b} = \begin{pmatrix} 3 \\ 1 \end{pmatrix} + \begin{pmatrix} -1 \\ 2 \end{pmatrix}$

$= \begin{pmatrix} 3 + -1 \\ 1 + 2 \end{pmatrix} = \begin{pmatrix} 2 \\ 3 \end{pmatrix}$

The vector $\mathbf{a} + \mathbf{b}$ is equivalent to vector $\mathbf{a}$ followed by vector $\mathbf{b}$.

iii) $\mathbf{a} - \mathbf{b} = \begin{pmatrix} 3 \\ 1 \end{pmatrix} - \begin{pmatrix} -1 \\ 2 \end{pmatrix}$

$= \begin{pmatrix} 3 - (-1) \\ 1 - 2 \end{pmatrix} = \begin{pmatrix} 4 \\ -1 \end{pmatrix}$

The vector $\mathbf{a} - \mathbf{b}$ is equivalent to vector $\mathbf{a}$ followed by vector $-\mathbf{b}$, which is in the opposite direction to $\mathbf{b}$.

Position vectors

The position vector of a point P, written $\overrightarrow{OP}$ or $\mathbf{p}$, is the vector from the origin, O, to that point. The point O is not always shown in diagrams.

The magnitude of a vector

The magnitude of a vector can be found using Pythagoras' theorem.

So, for example, the magnitude of the vector $-5\mathbf{i} + 2\mathbf{j}$ is

$\sqrt{(-5)^2 + 2^2} = \sqrt{25 + 4} = \sqrt{29}$.

Vectors

EXAMPLE 2

The points A and B have co-ordinates $(5, -1)$ and $(2, 3)$.

i) Find the vector $\overrightarrow{AB}$.

ii) Find the magnitude of the vector $\overrightarrow{AB}$.

iii) Write down a unit vector in the direction of the vector $\overrightarrow{BA}$.

SOLUTION

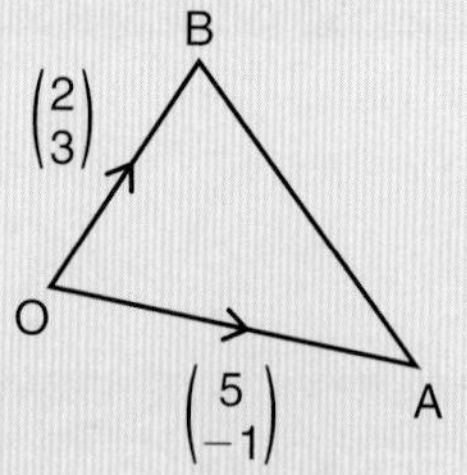

i) $\overrightarrow{AB} = \overrightarrow{AO} + \overrightarrow{OB} = -\overrightarrow{OA} + \overrightarrow{OB}$

$= -\begin{pmatrix} 5 \\ -1 \end{pmatrix} + \begin{pmatrix} 2 \\ 3 \end{pmatrix} = \begin{pmatrix} -5+2 \\ -(-1)+3 \end{pmatrix} = \begin{pmatrix} -3 \\ 4 \end{pmatrix}$

ii) $|\overrightarrow{AB}| = \sqrt{(-3)^2 + 4^2} = \sqrt{9+16} = \sqrt{25} = 5$

iii) $\overrightarrow{BA} = -\overrightarrow{AB} = \begin{pmatrix} 3 \\ -4 \end{pmatrix}$

Since this vector has magnitude 5, the unit vector in this direction

is $\frac{1}{5}\begin{pmatrix} 3 \\ -4 \end{pmatrix} = \begin{pmatrix} \frac{3}{5} \\ -\frac{4}{5} \end{pmatrix}$.

Geometry using vectors

EXAMPLE 3

The diagram shows a parallelogram ABCD.
$\overrightarrow{AB} = \mathbf{p}$ and $\overrightarrow{AD} = \mathbf{q}$.

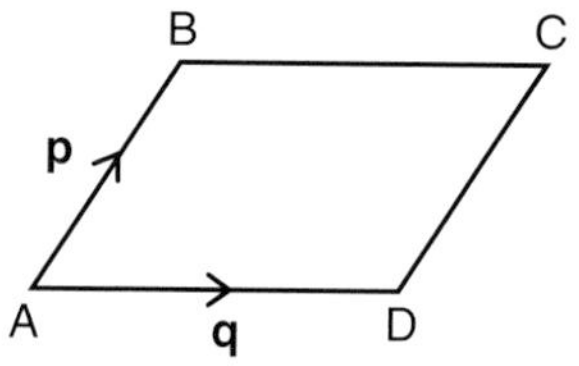

i) Find, in terms of $\mathbf{p}$ and $\mathbf{q}$, the vectors $\overrightarrow{AC}$ and $\overrightarrow{BD}$.

ii) The point M is the mid-point of BD. Find the vector $\overrightarrow{AM}$.

iii) The point N is $\frac{1}{3}$ of the way along AC. Find the vector $\overrightarrow{DN}$.

SOLUTION

i) $\overrightarrow{AC} = \overrightarrow{AB} + \overrightarrow{BC} = \mathbf{p} + \mathbf{q}$

As ABCD is a parallelogram, $\overrightarrow{BC} = \overrightarrow{AD} = \mathbf{q}$.

$\overrightarrow{BD} = \overrightarrow{BA} + \overrightarrow{AD} = -\mathbf{p} + \mathbf{q} = \mathbf{q} - \mathbf{p}$

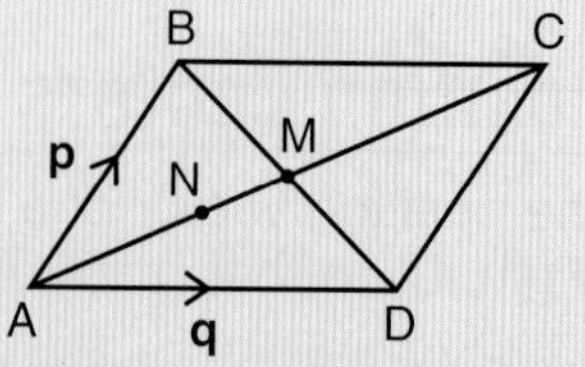

ii) $\overrightarrow{BM} = \frac{1}{2}\overrightarrow{BD} = \frac{1}{2}(\mathbf{q} - \mathbf{p})$

$\overrightarrow{AM} = \overrightarrow{AB} + \overrightarrow{BM} = \mathbf{p} + \frac{1}{2}(\mathbf{q} - \mathbf{p}) = \mathbf{p} + \frac{1}{2}\mathbf{q} - \frac{1}{2}\mathbf{p} = \frac{1}{2}\mathbf{p} + \frac{1}{2}\mathbf{q}$

iii) $\overrightarrow{AN} = \frac{1}{3}\overrightarrow{AC} = \frac{1}{3}(\mathbf{p} + \mathbf{q})$

$\overrightarrow{DN} = \overrightarrow{DA} + \overrightarrow{AN} = -\mathbf{q} + \frac{1}{3}(\mathbf{p} + \mathbf{q}) = -\mathbf{q} + \frac{1}{3}\mathbf{p} + \frac{1}{3}\mathbf{q} = \frac{1}{3}\mathbf{p} - \frac{2}{3}\mathbf{q}$

Vectors in three dimensions

A vector in three dimensions can be described using components in the x, y and z directions. In addition to the unit vectors **i** and **j**, the unit vector in the z direction is denoted by **k**.

The magnitude of a vector in three dimensions can be found by extending Pythagoras' theorem. So, for example, the magnitude of the vector $3\mathbf{i} + \mathbf{j} - 2\mathbf{k}$ is $\sqrt{3^2 + 1^2 + (-2)^2} = \sqrt{9 + 1 + 4} = \sqrt{14}$.

✓

EXAMPLE 4

Three points A, B and C have co-ordinates $(1, -2, 0), (1, 3, -2)$ and $(3, 0, 2)$.

i) Find the vectors $\overrightarrow{AB}$ and $\overrightarrow{BC}$.

ii) Show that the triangle ABC is isosceles.

iii) M is the mid-point of BC. Find the position vector of M.

SOLUTION

i) $\overrightarrow{AB} = \overrightarrow{AO} + \overrightarrow{OB} = \overrightarrow{OB} - \overrightarrow{OA} = \begin{pmatrix} 1 \\ 3 \\ -2 \end{pmatrix} - \begin{pmatrix} 1 \\ -2 \\ 0 \end{pmatrix} = \begin{pmatrix} 0 \\ 5 \\ -2 \end{pmatrix}$

$\overrightarrow{BC} = \overrightarrow{BO} + \overrightarrow{OC} = \overrightarrow{OC} - \overrightarrow{OB} = \begin{pmatrix} 3 \\ 0 \\ 2 \end{pmatrix} - \begin{pmatrix} 1 \\ 3 \\ -2 \end{pmatrix} = \begin{pmatrix} 2 \\ -3 \\ 4 \end{pmatrix}$

ii) $|\overrightarrow{AB}| = \sqrt{0^2 + 5^2 + (-2)^2} = \sqrt{25 + 4} = \sqrt{29}$

$|\overrightarrow{BC}| = \sqrt{2^2 + (-3)^2 + 4^2} = \sqrt{4 + 9 + 16} = \sqrt{29}$

Since the lengths of AB and BC are equal, the triangle is isosceles.

iii) $\overrightarrow{BM} = \frac{1}{2}\overrightarrow{BC} = \frac{1}{2}\begin{pmatrix} 2 \\ -3 \\ 4 \end{pmatrix} = \begin{pmatrix} 1 \\ -\frac{3}{2} \\ 2 \end{pmatrix}$

$\overrightarrow{OM} = \overrightarrow{OB} + \overrightarrow{BM} = \begin{pmatrix} 1 \\ 3 \\ -2 \end{pmatrix} + \begin{pmatrix} 1 \\ -\frac{3}{2} \\ 2 \end{pmatrix} = \begin{pmatrix} 2 \\ \frac{3}{2} \\ 0 \end{pmatrix}$

LINKS

Pure Mathematics
Mechanics

Work on vectors is developed further in FP3.
Vectors are used extensively in Mechanics when working in 2-D or 3-D. They are often used to represent displacements, velocities, accelerations and forces.

Test Yourself >L

1 The vectors **p** and **q** are given by **p** = 2**i** − **j** + 3**k** and **q** = 3**i** + 2**j** − 4**k**.
  Find the vector 3**p** − 2**q**.

  A **j** − **k**　　　　　　B **j** + **k**　　　　　　C −7**j** + 17**k**　　　　　　D −7**j** + **k**

Questions **2, 3, 4** and **5** are about three points A, B and C which have co-ordinates $(1, 0, 3)$, $(3, 1, -4)$ and $(-2, 6, 5)$, respectively.

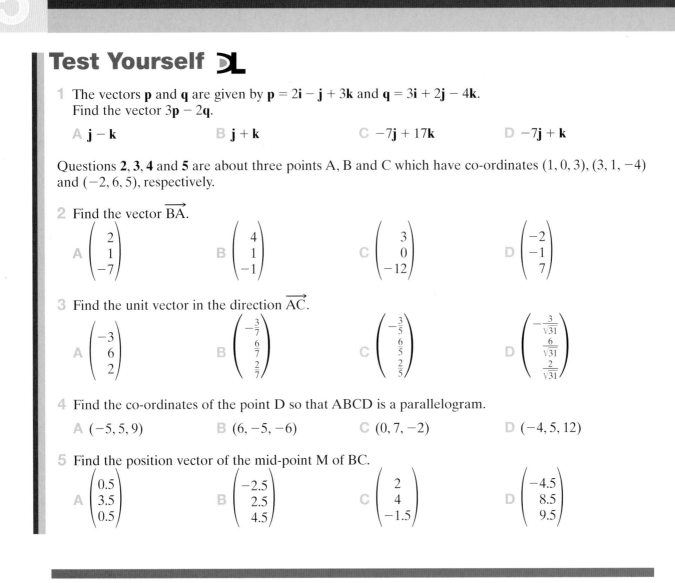

2 Find the vector $\overrightarrow{BA}$.

  A $\begin{pmatrix} 2 \\ 1 \\ -7 \end{pmatrix}$　　　　B $\begin{pmatrix} 4 \\ 1 \\ -1 \end{pmatrix}$　　　　C $\begin{pmatrix} 3 \\ 0 \\ -12 \end{pmatrix}$　　　　D $\begin{pmatrix} -2 \\ -1 \\ 7 \end{pmatrix}$

3 Find the unit vector in the direction $\overrightarrow{AC}$.

  A $\begin{pmatrix} -3 \\ 6 \\ 2 \end{pmatrix}$　　　　B $\begin{pmatrix} -\frac{3}{7} \\ \frac{6}{7} \\ \frac{2}{7} \end{pmatrix}$　　　　C $\begin{pmatrix} -\frac{3}{5} \\ \frac{6}{5} \\ \frac{2}{5} \end{pmatrix}$　　　　D $\begin{pmatrix} -\frac{3}{\sqrt{31}} \\ \frac{6}{\sqrt{31}} \\ \frac{2}{\sqrt{31}} \end{pmatrix}$

4 Find the co-ordinates of the point D so that ABCD is a parallelogram.

  A $(-5, 5, 9)$　　　　B $(6, -5, -6)$　　　　C $(0, 7, -2)$　　　　D $(-4, 5, 12)$

5 Find the position vector of the mid-point M of BC.

  A $\begin{pmatrix} 0.5 \\ 3.5 \\ 0.5 \end{pmatrix}$　　　　B $\begin{pmatrix} -2.5 \\ 2.5 \\ 4.5 \end{pmatrix}$　　　　C $\begin{pmatrix} 2 \\ 4 \\ -1.5 \end{pmatrix}$　　　　D $\begin{pmatrix} -4.5 \\ 8.5 \\ 9.5 \end{pmatrix}$

Exam-Style Question >L

Two points A and B have co-ordinates $(4, -1, 3)$ and $(0, 3, 1)$, respectively.

i) Find the vector $\overrightarrow{AB}$.

ii) The point C is such that $\overrightarrow{AC}$ has the same magnitude as $\overrightarrow{AB}$ and is parallel to the vector **i** + 2**j** − 2**k**. Find the vector $\overrightarrow{AC}$.

iii) Hence find the co-ordinates of C.

iv) D is the mid-point of AC. Find the position vector of D.

v) The median M of triangle ABC is the point $\frac{1}{3}$ of the way along DB. Find the co-ordinates of M.

Vector equations of lines

Vectors often provide easier methods of solving problems in co-ordinate geometry than the approaches you used in C1, particularly when working in 3-D. To solve problems involving straight lines using vector methods, you need to be able to find and work with the equation of a line in vector form.

- The equation of a line in cartesian form from C1.

- The vector equation of a line passing through the point with position vector **a**, and parallel to the vector **u**, is given by $\mathbf{r} = \mathbf{a} + \lambda\mathbf{u}$.
- The equivalent cartesian form for a line in three dimensions is

$$\frac{x - a_1}{u_1} = \frac{y - a_2}{u_2} = \frac{z - a_3}{u_3}.$$

The vector equation of a line

The equation of a straight line, in 2- or 3-D, can be written in the form $\mathbf{r} = \mathbf{a} + \lambda\mathbf{u}$, where **a** is the position vector of any point on the line, and **u** is any vector parallel to the line (often called the **direction vector**). Each different value of the parameter λ (which need not be a whole number) corresponds to a different point on the line.

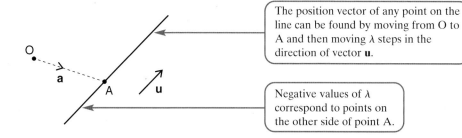

The position vector of any point on the line can be found by moving from O to A and then moving λ steps in the direction of vector **u**.

Negative values of λ correspond to points on the other side of point A.

You can write the equation of a line using column vectors, for example

$\mathbf{r} = \begin{pmatrix} 1 \\ 2 \\ 0 \end{pmatrix} + \lambda\begin{pmatrix} -2 \\ 3 \\ 1 \end{pmatrix}$, or in the form $\mathbf{r} = \mathbf{i} + 2\mathbf{j} + \lambda(-2\mathbf{i} + 3\mathbf{j} + \mathbf{k})$.

EXAMPLE 1

i) Write down a vector equation of the line through the point $(3, 1, 2)$ parallel to the vector $\mathbf{i} - \mathbf{j} + 2\mathbf{k}$.

ii) Find out whether the point $(0, 4, -3)$ lies on the line.

SOLUTION

Position vector of the point on the line.　Direction vector of the line.

i) An equation of the line is $\mathbf{r} = \begin{pmatrix} 3 \\ 1 \\ 2 \end{pmatrix} + \lambda \begin{pmatrix} 1 \\ -1 \\ 2 \end{pmatrix}$.

ii) If the point $(0, 4, -3)$ lies on the line, then there is a value of λ for

which $\begin{pmatrix} 3 \\ 1 \\ 2 \end{pmatrix} + \lambda \begin{pmatrix} 1 \\ -1 \\ 2 \end{pmatrix} = \begin{pmatrix} 0 \\ 4 \\ -3 \end{pmatrix}$

$\lambda \begin{pmatrix} 1 \\ -1 \\ 2 \end{pmatrix} = \begin{pmatrix} 0 \\ 4 \\ -3 \end{pmatrix} - \begin{pmatrix} 3 \\ 1 \\ 2 \end{pmatrix} = \begin{pmatrix} -3 \\ 3 \\ -5 \end{pmatrix}$ ← For the top two rows, $\lambda = -3$ satisfies the equation, but for the third row, $\lambda = -2.5$ is needed.

There is no value of λ which satisfies this equation, so the point $(0, 4, -3)$ does not lie on the line.

EXAMPLE 2

Find a vector equation for the line joining the points $P(1, 2, -3)$ and $Q(4, 0, 1)$.

SOLUTION

The equation of the line is $\mathbf{r} = \mathbf{a} + \lambda\mathbf{u}$.

$\mathbf{a}$ is the position vector of a point on the line.

Using P gives $\mathbf{a} = \begin{pmatrix} 1 \\ 2 \\ -3 \end{pmatrix}$.

$\mathbf{u}$ is the direction vector of the line.

$\overrightarrow{PQ} = \overrightarrow{OQ} - \overrightarrow{OP} = \begin{pmatrix} 4 \\ 0 \\ 1 \end{pmatrix} - \begin{pmatrix} 1 \\ 2 \\ -3 \end{pmatrix} = \begin{pmatrix} 3 \\ -2 \\ 4 \end{pmatrix}$

So the equation of the line is $\mathbf{r} = \begin{pmatrix} 1 \\ 2 \\ -3 \end{pmatrix} + \lambda \begin{pmatrix} 3 \\ -2 \\ 4 \end{pmatrix}$.

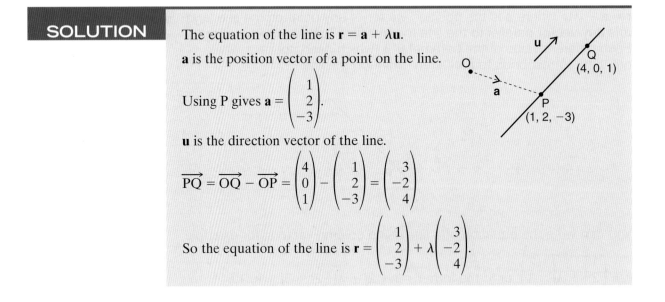

It is important to realise that there are infinitely many vector equations for the same line. You could choose any point on the line for the vector $\mathbf{a}$, and vector $\mathbf{u}$ could be any scalar multiple of the direction vector. In Example 2 above, you could have used point Q instead of point P for vector $\mathbf{a}$, and you could have used $\overrightarrow{QP}$ instead of $\overrightarrow{PQ}$ for vector $\mathbf{u}$. It is usually best to use the direction vector in its simplest possible form, so divide through by any common factor.

✓

EXAMPLE 3

Show that the lines $\mathbf{r} = \begin{pmatrix} 3 \\ -1 \\ 2 \end{pmatrix} + \lambda \begin{pmatrix} 4 \\ 0 \\ 1 \end{pmatrix}$ and $\mathbf{r} = \begin{pmatrix} 1 \\ -4 \\ 3 \end{pmatrix} + \mu \begin{pmatrix} -2 \\ 1 \\ -1 \end{pmatrix}$ intersect at

the point $(-5, -1, 0)$.

SOLUTION

If the point $(-5, -1, 0)$ lies on the line $\mathbf{r} = \begin{pmatrix} 3 \\ -1 \\ 2 \end{pmatrix} + \lambda \begin{pmatrix} 4 \\ 0 \\ 1 \end{pmatrix}$, then

$$\begin{pmatrix} 3 \\ -1 \\ 2 \end{pmatrix} + \lambda \begin{pmatrix} 4 \\ 0 \\ 1 \end{pmatrix} = \begin{pmatrix} -5 \\ -1 \\ 0 \end{pmatrix} \text{ for some value of } \lambda.$$

So $\lambda \begin{pmatrix} 4 \\ 0 \\ 1 \end{pmatrix} = \begin{pmatrix} -5 \\ -1 \\ 0 \end{pmatrix} - \begin{pmatrix} 3 \\ -1 \\ 2 \end{pmatrix} = \begin{pmatrix} -8 \\ 0 \\ -2 \end{pmatrix}.$

This equation is satisfied by $\lambda = -2$, so the point $(-5, -1, 0)$ lies on the line.

If the point $(-5, -1, 0)$ lies on the line $\mathbf{r} = \begin{pmatrix} 1 \\ -4 \\ 3 \end{pmatrix} + \mu \begin{pmatrix} -2 \\ 1 \\ -1 \end{pmatrix}$, then

$$\begin{pmatrix} 1 \\ -4 \\ 3 \end{pmatrix} + \mu \begin{pmatrix} -2 \\ 1 \\ -1 \end{pmatrix} = \begin{pmatrix} -5 \\ -1 \\ 0 \end{pmatrix} \text{ for some value of } \mu.$$

So $\mu \begin{pmatrix} -2 \\ 1 \\ -1 \end{pmatrix} = \begin{pmatrix} -5 \\ -1 \\ 0 \end{pmatrix} - \begin{pmatrix} 1 \\ -4 \\ 3 \end{pmatrix} = \begin{pmatrix} -6 \\ 3 \\ -3 \end{pmatrix}.$

This equation is satisfied by $\mu = 3$, so the point $(-5, -1, 0)$ lies on the line.

Since the point $(-5, -1, 0)$ lies on both lines, it is the intersection point of the lines.

Changing vector equations to cartesian equations

The line $\mathbf{r} = \begin{pmatrix} a_1 \\ a_2 \\ a_3 \end{pmatrix} + \lambda \begin{pmatrix} u_1 \\ u_2 \\ u_3 \end{pmatrix}$ can be expressed in cartesian form by writing

the equation as $\begin{pmatrix} x \\ y \\ z \end{pmatrix} = \begin{pmatrix} a_1 \\ a_2 \\ a_3 \end{pmatrix} + \lambda \begin{pmatrix} u_1 \\ u_2 \\ u_3 \end{pmatrix}$, so $\begin{pmatrix} x - a_1 \\ y - a_2 \\ z - a_3 \end{pmatrix} = \begin{pmatrix} \lambda u_1 \\ \lambda u_2 \\ \lambda u_3 \end{pmatrix}$. This can be

written as three separate equations: $x - a_1 = \lambda u_1$, $y - a_2 = \lambda u_2$ and $z - a_3 = \lambda u_3$. These give three separate expressions for λ which are all equal to each other.

So $\dfrac{x - a_1}{u_1} = \dfrac{y - a_2}{u_2} = \dfrac{z - a_3}{u_3} (= \lambda).$

This is the cartesian form of the equation of the line.

EXAMPLE 4

Write the equations of these lines in cartesian form.

    i) $\mathbf{r} = 2\mathbf{i} - 3\mathbf{k} + \lambda(\mathbf{i} + 4\mathbf{j} - 2\mathbf{k})$

    ii) $\mathbf{r} = \mathbf{i} - 3\mathbf{j} + 2\mathbf{k} + \lambda(2\mathbf{i} - \mathbf{j})$

SOLUTION

i) $\begin{pmatrix} x \\ y \\ z \end{pmatrix} = \begin{pmatrix} 2 \\ 0 \\ -3 \end{pmatrix} + \lambda \begin{pmatrix} 1 \\ 4 \\ -2 \end{pmatrix}$, so $\begin{pmatrix} x-2 \\ y \\ z+3 \end{pmatrix} = \begin{pmatrix} \lambda \\ 4\lambda \\ -2\lambda \end{pmatrix}$

The cartesian form of the equation is $x - 2 = \dfrac{y}{4} = \dfrac{z+3}{-2} = \lambda$.

ii) $\begin{pmatrix} x \\ y \\ z \end{pmatrix} = \begin{pmatrix} 1 \\ -3 \\ 2 \end{pmatrix} + \lambda \begin{pmatrix} 2 \\ -1 \\ 0 \end{pmatrix}$, so $\begin{pmatrix} x-1 \\ y+3 \\ z-2 \end{pmatrix} = \begin{pmatrix} 2\lambda \\ -\lambda \\ 0 \end{pmatrix}$

> Since there is no **k** component in the direction vector, z must be 2 for all points on the line. So this part of the equation must be omitted, and $z = 2$ written as part of the equation.

The equation of the line is $z = 2$ and $\dfrac{x-1}{2} = \dfrac{y+3}{-1} = \lambda$.

Changing cartesian equations to vector equations

This process can easily be reversed to write the cartesian equation of a line in vector form.

The cartesian equation $\dfrac{x - a_1}{u_1} = \dfrac{y - a_2}{u_2} = \dfrac{z - a_3}{u_3} = \lambda$ can be written

as the three equations $x - a_1 = \lambda u_1$, $y - a_2 = \lambda u_2$ and $z - a_3 = \lambda u_3$.

This can be written as the vector equation $\begin{pmatrix} x \\ y \\ z \end{pmatrix} = \begin{pmatrix} a_1 \\ a_2 \\ a_3 \end{pmatrix} + \lambda \begin{pmatrix} u_1 \\ u_2 \\ u_3 \end{pmatrix}$.

EXAMPLE 5

Write the equation of the line $\dfrac{x - 1}{2} = \dfrac{y}{3} = \dfrac{z + 3}{-4}$ in vector form.

SOLUTION

The equation $\dfrac{x - 1}{2} = \dfrac{y}{3} = \dfrac{z + 3}{-4} = \lambda$ can be written as

$$\begin{array}{ll} x - 1 = 2\lambda & \text{or} \quad x = 1 + 2\lambda \\ y = 3\lambda & \qquad\;\; y = 3\lambda \\ z + 3 = -4\lambda & \qquad\;\; z = -3 - 4\lambda \end{array}$$

In vector form this is $\begin{pmatrix} x \\ y \\ z \end{pmatrix} = \begin{pmatrix} 1 \\ 0 \\ -3 \end{pmatrix} + \lambda \begin{pmatrix} 2 \\ 3 \\ -4 \end{pmatrix}$.

So the equation of the line in vector form is $\mathbf{r} = \begin{pmatrix} 1 \\ 0 \\ -3 \end{pmatrix} + \lambda \begin{pmatrix} 2 \\ 3 \\ -4 \end{pmatrix}$.

LINKS

Pure Mathematics   Further work on vector equations of lines, including finding distances between lines and the distance of a point from a line, is covered in FP3.

Test Yourself ▶L

1 Which one of these points does **not** lie on the line $\mathbf{r} = 4\mathbf{i} + \mathbf{j} - 2\mathbf{k} + \lambda(2\mathbf{i} - 3\mathbf{j} + \mathbf{k})$?

   A $(2, 4, -3)$ B $(6, -2, -1)$ C $(8, -5, 0)$ D $(4, 1, -2)$ E $(0, 5, -4)$

2 Which one of the equations below describes the line through the points $P(2, 5, -1)$ and $Q(0, -1, 3)$?

   A $\mathbf{r} = \begin{pmatrix} -2 \\ -6 \\ 4 \end{pmatrix} + \lambda \begin{pmatrix} 2 \\ 5 \\ -1 \end{pmatrix}$ B $\mathbf{r} = \begin{pmatrix} 0 \\ -1 \\ 3 \end{pmatrix} + \lambda \begin{pmatrix} 1 \\ 3 \\ -2 \end{pmatrix}$ C $\mathbf{r} = \begin{pmatrix} 0 \\ -1 \\ 3 \end{pmatrix} + \lambda \begin{pmatrix} 2 \\ 5 \\ -1 \end{pmatrix}$ D $\mathbf{r} = \begin{pmatrix} 2 \\ 5 \\ -1 \end{pmatrix} + \lambda \begin{pmatrix} 0 \\ -1 \\ 3 \end{pmatrix}$

3 What is an equation for the line $\dfrac{x+3}{2} = \dfrac{y-4}{1} = \dfrac{z}{-3}$ in vector form?

   A $\mathbf{r} = \begin{pmatrix} 2 \\ 1 \\ -3 \end{pmatrix} + \lambda \begin{pmatrix} -3 \\ 4 \\ 0 \end{pmatrix}$ B $\mathbf{r} = \begin{pmatrix} 3 \\ 4 \\ 0 \end{pmatrix} + \lambda \begin{pmatrix} 2 \\ 1 \\ -3 \end{pmatrix}$ C $\mathbf{r} = \begin{pmatrix} -3 \\ 4 \\ 0 \end{pmatrix} + \lambda \begin{pmatrix} 2 \\ 1 \\ -3 \end{pmatrix}$ D $\mathbf{r} = \begin{pmatrix} 2 \\ 1 \\ -3 \end{pmatrix} + \lambda \begin{pmatrix} 3 \\ 4 \\ 0 \end{pmatrix}$

4 The points P, Q and R have co-ordinates $(2, 1, -3)$, $(0, 4, 3)$ and $(1, 2, -1)$ respectively. A straight line passes through P and is parallel to QR. Which one of the equations below is a cartesian equation for this line?

   A $\dfrac{x-2}{1} = \dfrac{y-1}{-2} = \dfrac{z+3}{-4}$ B $\dfrac{x-1}{2} = \dfrac{y+2}{1} = \dfrac{z+4}{-3}$

   C $\dfrac{x+2}{1} = \dfrac{y+1}{-2} = \dfrac{z-3}{-4}$ D $\dfrac{x+1}{2} = \dfrac{y-2}{1} = \dfrac{z-4}{-3}$

5 Which of these points is the intersection point of the line $\mathbf{r} = 2\mathbf{i} - \mathbf{j} + \lambda(\mathbf{i} + 3\mathbf{j} - 2\mathbf{k})$ and the line $\mathbf{r} = 3\mathbf{i} - 2\mathbf{j} + 4\mathbf{k} + \mu(-2\mathbf{i} - 4\mathbf{j} + \mathbf{k})$?

   A $(3, -2, 2)$ B $(0, -7, -4)$ C $(0, 5, -2)$ D $(-1, -10, 6)$

Exam-Style Question ▶L

i) The points A and B have co-ordinates $(2, -1, -2)$ and $(3, 1, -4)$, respectively. Write down an equation for the line AB in vector form.

ii) Another line has cartesian equation $\dfrac{x-1}{-1} = \dfrac{y+3}{-2} = \dfrac{z}{2}$.

   Write the equation of this line in vector form.

iii) Show that these two lines meet at the point P with co-ordinates $(4, 3, -6)$.

iv) The point C lies on the line AB, and is nearer to B than to A. Given that the length of AC is 12 units, find the co-ordinates of C.

The scalar product

It is often useful to be able to find the angle between two vectors or two lines. The scalar product provides a method of doing this, usually much more quickly and easily than using trigonometry.

- The work on vectors, in particular the magnitude of a vector, from chapter 11 of C4.

- The scalar product of two vectors $\mathbf{a} = a_1\mathbf{i} + a_2\mathbf{j} + a_3\mathbf{k}$ and $\mathbf{b} = b_1\mathbf{i} + b_2\mathbf{j} + b_3\mathbf{k}$ is written as $\mathbf{a.b}$ and is given by $a_1b_1 + a_2b_2 + a_3b_3$.
- $\mathbf{a.b} = |\mathbf{a}||\mathbf{b}| \cos \theta$, where θ is the angle between vectors $\mathbf{a}$ and $\mathbf{b}$.
- The scalar product of two perpendicular vectors is zero.
- The angle between two lines is the angle between the direction vectors of the lines.

The scalar product

The scalar product (or dot product) of two vectors $\mathbf{a} = a_1\mathbf{i} + a_2\mathbf{j} + a_3\mathbf{k}$ and $\mathbf{b} = b_1\mathbf{i} + b_2\mathbf{j} + b_3\mathbf{k}$ is written as $\mathbf{a.b}$ and is given by

$$\mathbf{a.b} = a_1b_1 + a_2b_2 + a_3b_3$$

EXAMPLE 1   Find the scalar product of $\mathbf{a} = 2\mathbf{i} - 3\mathbf{j} + 4\mathbf{k}$ and $\mathbf{b} = 3\mathbf{i} - \mathbf{j} - 2\mathbf{k}$.

SOLUTION

You may find it easier to write vectors in column vector form.

$$\mathbf{a.b} = \begin{pmatrix} 2 \\ -3 \\ 4 \end{pmatrix} \cdot \begin{pmatrix} 3 \\ -1 \\ -2 \end{pmatrix} = (2 \times 3) + (-3 \times -1) + (4 \times -2) = 6 + 3 - 8 = 1$$

Notice that the result of a scalar product is just a number (a scalar), not a vector. It may be positive or negative.

The angle between two vectors

The scalar product can also be written in the form

$$\mathbf{a.b} = |\mathbf{a}||\mathbf{b}| \cos \theta$$

Remember that $|\mathbf{a}|$ and $|\mathbf{b}|$ are the magnitudes, or lengths, of the vectors $\mathbf{a}$ and $\mathbf{b}$.

where θ is the angle between vectors $\mathbf{a}$ and $\mathbf{b}$.

This formula allows you to find the angle between two vectors.

You can rearrange the formula into the form $\cos \theta = \dfrac{\mathbf{a.b}}{|\mathbf{a}||\mathbf{b}|}$.

✓ **EXAMPLE 2**   Find the angle between the two vectors $\mathbf{a} = -4\mathbf{i} + \mathbf{j} - 2\mathbf{k}$ and $\mathbf{b} = 2\mathbf{i} + 3\mathbf{j} + 5\mathbf{k}$.

SOLUTION

$$\mathbf{a.b} = \begin{pmatrix} -4 \\ 1 \\ -2 \end{pmatrix} \cdot \begin{pmatrix} 2 \\ 3 \\ 5 \end{pmatrix} = (-4 \times 2) + (1 \times 3) + (-2 \times 5) = -8 + 3 - 10$$
$$= -15$$

$$|\mathbf{a}| = \sqrt{(-4)^2 + 1^2 + (-2)^2} = \sqrt{16 + 1 + 4} = \sqrt{21}$$

$$|\mathbf{b}| = \sqrt{2^2 + 3^2 + 5^2} = \sqrt{4 + 9 + 25} = \sqrt{38}$$

$$\cos\theta = \frac{\mathbf{a.b}}{|\mathbf{a}||\mathbf{b}|} = \frac{-15}{\sqrt{21}\,\sqrt{38}}$$

$$\theta = 122.1° \text{ (1 d.p.)}$$

A ADVICE

Notice that in Example 2, the scalar product was negative, which meant that $\cos\theta$ was also negative, and so the angle between the two vectors was obtuse. If the scalar product is positive, then the angle between the two vectors is acute.

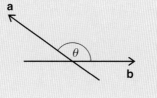

The angle between these two vectors $\mathbf{a}$ and $\mathbf{b}$ is obtuse, because you need the angle between the positive directions of the vectors. The acute angle between the vectors is the angle between $\mathbf{a}$ and $-\mathbf{b}$ (or $-\mathbf{a}$ and $\mathbf{b}$).

Perpendicular vectors

If two vectors are perpendicular, then the angle between them is 90°.
Since $\cos 90° = 0$, then the scalar product of two perpendicular vectors must be zero.

✓ **EXAMPLE 3**   Show that the vectors $\mathbf{p} = 3\mathbf{i} + 2\mathbf{j} - \mathbf{k}$ and $\mathbf{q} = 4\mathbf{i} - 3\mathbf{j} + 6\mathbf{k}$ are perpendicular.

SOLUTION

$$\mathbf{p.q} = \begin{pmatrix} 3 \\ 2 \\ -1 \end{pmatrix} \cdot \begin{pmatrix} 4 \\ -3 \\ 6 \end{pmatrix} = (3 \times 4) + (2 \times -3) + (-1 \times 6) = 12 - 6 - 6 = 0$$

Since the scalar product of $\mathbf{p}$ and $\mathbf{q}$ is zero, the vectors are perpendicular.

A ADVICE

If you are asked to show that two vectors are perpendicular, you must show all the intermediate working, as in the example above, otherwise you will lose marks.

The angle between two lines

The angle between two lines is the angle between the direction vectors of the lines.

EXAMPLE 4

i) Find the angle between the lines $\mathbf{r} = \begin{pmatrix} -4 \\ 0 \\ 1 \end{pmatrix} + \lambda \begin{pmatrix} 1 \\ 2 \\ -4 \end{pmatrix}$ and

$$\mathbf{r} = \begin{pmatrix} 2 \\ 1 \\ -3 \end{pmatrix} + \mu \begin{pmatrix} 5 \\ -1 \\ 0 \end{pmatrix}.$$

ii) Find the angle between the lines $\mathbf{r} = \begin{pmatrix} 3 \\ 0 \\ 2 \end{pmatrix} + \lambda \begin{pmatrix} 1 \\ 2 \\ -4 \end{pmatrix}$ and

$$\mathbf{r} = \begin{pmatrix} 2 \\ 1 \\ -3 \end{pmatrix} + \mu \begin{pmatrix} 5 \\ -1 \\ 0 \end{pmatrix}.$$

SOLUTION

i) The angle between the lines is the angle between the direction vectors

$$\begin{pmatrix} 1 \\ 2 \\ -4 \end{pmatrix} \text{ and } \begin{pmatrix} 5 \\ -1 \\ 0 \end{pmatrix}.$$

$$\mathbf{a.b} = \begin{pmatrix} 1 \\ 2 \\ -4 \end{pmatrix} \cdot \begin{pmatrix} 5 \\ -1 \\ 0 \end{pmatrix} = (1 \times 5) + (2 \times -1) + (-4 \times 0) = 5 - 2 + 0 = 3$$

$$|\mathbf{a}| = \sqrt{1^2 + 2^2 + (-4)^2} = \sqrt{1 + 4 + 16} = \sqrt{21}$$

$$|\mathbf{b}| = \sqrt{5^2 + (-1)^2 + 0^2} = \sqrt{25 + 1 + 0} = \sqrt{26}$$

$$\cos \theta = \frac{\mathbf{a.b}}{|\mathbf{a}||\mathbf{b}|} = \frac{3}{\sqrt{21}\sqrt{26}}$$

$$\theta = 82.6° \text{ (1 d.p.)}$$

The angle between the lines is 82.6°.

> These lines meet at the point $(-3, 2, -3)$.

ii) These lines do not meet, but their directions are the same as before, so the angle is the same.

The angle between the lines is 82.6°.

> Of course the scalar product and angle calculation is identical in each case.

A ADVICE

In part i) of the example above, the equation of the second line could have been given in the equivalent form $\mathbf{r} = \begin{pmatrix} 2 \\ 1 \\ -3 \end{pmatrix} + \mu \begin{pmatrix} -5 \\ 1 \\ 0 \end{pmatrix}$. This would give a negative scalar product and therefore an obtuse angle between the two lines. In examination questions, you will often be asked to give the *acute* angle between two lines, so if your scalar product turns out to be negative, and you have been asked for the acute angle, you should take the positive value.

LINKS

Pure Mathematics   Further work on products involving vectors in FP3.

Test Yourself ⊃L

1 Find the scalar product of the vectors $\mathbf{a} = -2\mathbf{i} + 3\mathbf{j} - \mathbf{k}$ and $\mathbf{b} = \mathbf{i} - 3\mathbf{k}$.

A -11 B 1 C -5 D 4

2 Find the angle between the vectors $\mathbf{p} = \begin{pmatrix} 3 \\ 1 \\ -4 \end{pmatrix}$ and $\mathbf{q} = \begin{pmatrix} 2 \\ -3 \\ -1 \end{pmatrix}$.

A $68.5°$ B $1.2°$ C $89.4°$ D $93.0°$

3 Which one of the vectors below is perpendicular to the vector $3\mathbf{i} - 4\mathbf{j} + \mathbf{k}$?

A $2\mathbf{i} - \mathbf{j} - 2\mathbf{k}$ B $4\mathbf{i} + 3\mathbf{k}$ C $-3\mathbf{i} - 4\mathbf{j} + 25\mathbf{k}$ D $-3\mathbf{i} - \mathbf{j} + 5\mathbf{k}$

4 The points P, Q and R have co-ordinates $(3, -2, 1)$, $(1, -3, 4)$ and $(-3, 0, 3)$ respectively. Find the angle PQR.

A $84°$ B $96°$ C $101°$ D $50°$

5 Find the acute angle between the lines $\mathbf{r} = \begin{pmatrix} 1 \\ 2 \\ 0 \end{pmatrix} + \lambda \begin{pmatrix} 2 \\ 3 \\ -1 \end{pmatrix}$ and $\mathbf{r} = \begin{pmatrix} 2 \\ -3 \\ 0 \end{pmatrix} + \mu \begin{pmatrix} -4 \\ 1 \\ -2 \end{pmatrix}$.

A $100°$ B $60°$ C $80°$ D $66°$

Exam-Style Question ⊃L

Three points P, Q and R have co-ordinates $(-4, 2, -2)$, $(1, -2, -5)$ and $(2, 0, -6)$, respectively.

i)   Show that PQ is perpendicular to QR.

ii) Hence find the exact area of triangle PQR.

iii) Find the angle QRP.

Planes

A | ABOUT THIS TOPIC

When working in three dimensions, you may need to work with planes, as well as with lines and points. In this section you look at the vector and cartesian equation of a plane, and solve problems involving lines and planes.

R | REMEMBER

- The vector equation of a line from C4.

- The cartesian equation of the plane is given by $n_1 x + n_2 y + n_3 z = d$, where $\begin{pmatrix} n_1 \\ n_2 \\ n_3 \end{pmatrix}$ is a vector perpendicular to the plane.

- A vector perpendicular to a plane is perpendicular to every line in the plane.

- To prove a vector is perpendicular to a plane you need to show it is perpendicular to two non-parallel lines in the plane.

- The angle between two planes is the angle between their normal vectors.

- The intersection point of a line and a plane can be found by substituting the equation of the line into the equation of the plane, and solving for λ.

- The vector equation of a plane is given by $\mathbf{r.n} = \mathbf{a.n}$, where $\mathbf{n} = n_1 \mathbf{i} + n_2 \mathbf{j} + n_3 \mathbf{k}$ is a vector perpendicular to the plane, and $\mathbf{a}$ is the position vector of a point on the plane.

The cartesian equation of a plane

It is usually easiest to work with the equation of a plane in cartesian form.

This has the form $n_1 x + n_2 y + n_3 z = d$.

So, for example, $2x + 3y + 4z = 19$ is a plane.

The vector $\begin{pmatrix} n_1 \\ n_2 \\ n_3 \end{pmatrix}$ is perpendicular to the plane $n_1 x + n_2 y + n_3 z = d$.

So $\begin{pmatrix} 2 \\ 3 \\ 4 \end{pmatrix}$ is perpendicular to the plane $2x + 3y + 4z = 19$.

A vector perpendicular to a plane is perpendicular to every line in the plane.

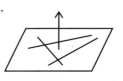

✓ **EXAMPLE 1**

The points A and B have co-ordinates $(2, 0, -1)$ and $(5, -1, 3)$.

Find, in cartesian form, the equation of the plane which contains point A and is perpendicular to the line AB.

SOLUTION

$$\overrightarrow{AB} = \overrightarrow{OB} - \overrightarrow{OA} = \begin{pmatrix} 5 \\ -1 \\ 3 \end{pmatrix} - \begin{pmatrix} 2 \\ 0 \\ -1 \end{pmatrix} = \begin{pmatrix} 3 \\ -1 \\ 4 \end{pmatrix}$$ and this is the normal vector

to the plane.

The equation of the plane is $3x - y + 4z = d$.

The point $A(2, 0, -1)$ lies on the plane, so $\quad 3 \times 2 - 0 + 4 \times -1 = d$

$$6 - 4 = d$$
$$2 = d$$

The equation of the plane is $3x - y + 4z = 2$.

The angle between two planes

The angle between two planes is the same as the angle between their normal vectors.

As with lines, there are two possible angles between a pair of planes, and it is usual to take the acute angle.

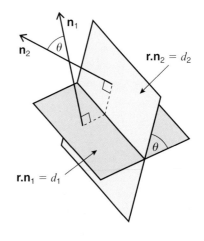

✓ **EXAMPLE 2**

Find the angle between the planes $2x - 3y + z = 4$ and $5x - 2y - 4z = 1$.

SOLUTION

The normal vectors for these planes are $\mathbf{n}_1 = \begin{pmatrix} 2 \\ -3 \\ 1 \end{pmatrix}$ and $\mathbf{n}_2 = \begin{pmatrix} 5 \\ -2 \\ -4 \end{pmatrix}$.

$$\mathbf{n}_1.\mathbf{n}_2 = \begin{pmatrix} 2 \\ -3 \\ 1 \end{pmatrix} \cdot \begin{pmatrix} 5 \\ -2 \\ -4 \end{pmatrix} = (2 \times 5) + (-3 \times -2) + (1 \times -4) = 10 + 6 - 4 = 12$$

$$|\mathbf{n}_1| = \sqrt{2^2 + (-3)^2 + 1^2} = \sqrt{4 + 9 + 1} = \sqrt{14}$$
$$|\mathbf{n}_2| = \sqrt{5^2 + (-2)^2 + (-4)^2} = \sqrt{25 + 4 + 16} = \sqrt{45}$$

$$\cos \theta = \frac{\mathbf{n}_1.\mathbf{n}_2}{|\mathbf{n}_1||\mathbf{n}_2|} = \frac{12}{\sqrt{14}\sqrt{45}}$$

$$\theta = 61.4°$$

The angle between the planes is $61.4°$ (1 d.p.).

The intersection of a line and a plane

The point of intersection of a line and a plane can be found by substituting the equation of the line into the equation of the plane, and then solving. This is shown in the next example.

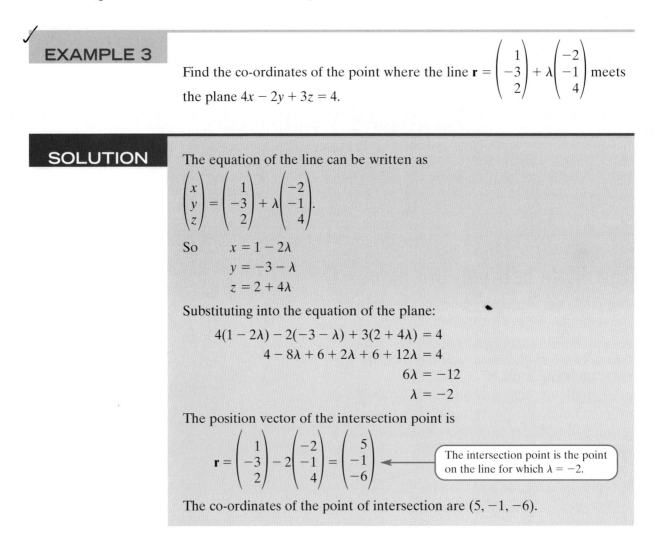

EXAMPLE 3

Find the co-ordinates of the point where the line $\mathbf{r} = \begin{pmatrix} 1 \\ -3 \\ 2 \end{pmatrix} + \lambda \begin{pmatrix} -2 \\ -1 \\ 4 \end{pmatrix}$ meets

the plane $4x - 2y + 3z = 4$.

SOLUTION

The equation of the line can be written as

$$\begin{pmatrix} x \\ y \\ z \end{pmatrix} = \begin{pmatrix} 1 \\ -3 \\ 2 \end{pmatrix} + \lambda \begin{pmatrix} -2 \\ -1 \\ 4 \end{pmatrix}.$$

So
$$x = 1 - 2\lambda$$
$$y = -3 - \lambda$$
$$z = 2 + 4\lambda$$

Substituting into the equation of the plane:
$$4(1 - 2\lambda) - 2(-3 - \lambda) + 3(2 + 4\lambda) = 4$$
$$4 - 8\lambda + 6 + 2\lambda + 6 + 12\lambda = 4$$
$$6\lambda = -12$$
$$\lambda = -2$$

The position vector of the intersection point is

$$\mathbf{r} = \begin{pmatrix} 1 \\ -3 \\ 2 \end{pmatrix} - 2\begin{pmatrix} -2 \\ -1 \\ 4 \end{pmatrix} = \begin{pmatrix} 5 \\ -1 \\ -6 \end{pmatrix} \quad \longleftarrow \boxed{\text{The intersection point is the point on the line for which } \lambda = -2.}$$

The co-ordinates of the point of intersection are $(5, -1, -6)$.

The vector equation of a plane

The equation of a plane can be defined in terms of the vector **n** which is perpendicular to the plane, and the position vector **a** of a point on the plane.

If the position vector of a general point on the plane is **r**, then the vector **r** − **a** lies in the plane. The vector **r** − **a** must therefore be perpendicular to the normal vector **n**, and so the scalar product of **r** − **a** and **n** must be zero.

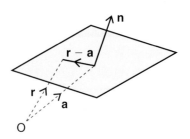

Therefore the equation of the plane can be written as
$(\mathbf{r} - \mathbf{a}).\mathbf{n} = 0$.

This is usually written as $\mathbf{r}.\mathbf{n} = \mathbf{a}.\mathbf{n}$

EXAMPLE 4

A plane contains the point $(3, 1, -4)$. The vector $2\mathbf{i} - 3\mathbf{j} + \mathbf{k}$ is perpendicular to the plane. Find the vector equation of the plane.

SOLUTION

The normal vector $\mathbf{n} = 2\mathbf{i} - 3\mathbf{j} + \mathbf{k}$.

The position vector of a point in the plane is $\mathbf{a} = 3\mathbf{i} + \mathbf{j} - 4\mathbf{k}$.

The equation of the plane is $\mathbf{r.n} = \mathbf{a.n}$

$$\mathbf{r}.(2\mathbf{i} - 3\mathbf{j} + \mathbf{k}) = (3\mathbf{i} + \mathbf{j} - 4\mathbf{k}).(2\mathbf{i} - 3\mathbf{j} + \mathbf{k})$$
$$= (3 \times 2) + (1 \times -3) + (-4 \times 1)$$
$$= 6 - 3 - 4$$
$$\mathbf{r}.(2\mathbf{i} - 3\mathbf{j} + \mathbf{k}) = -1$$

LINKS

Pure Mathematics   This work is developed further in the Vectors section of FP3, and is also used in the section on Multivariable calculus in FP3.

Test Yourself ▶L

1 Three points P, Q and R have co-ordinates $(1, 4, -2)$, $(5, 0, 1)$ and $(-3, 1, 4)$.
   What is the equation of the plane through P which is perpendicular to QR?

   A $8x - y - 3z + 10 = 0$ B $5x + z - 3 = 0$ C $3x - y - 4z - 7 = 0$ D $8x - y - 3z - 10 = 0$

2 Which one of these lines lies in the plane $5x - 2y + 3z = 4$?

   A $\mathbf{r} = \begin{pmatrix} 3 \\ 4 \\ -1 \end{pmatrix} + \lambda \begin{pmatrix} 5 \\ -2 \\ 3 \end{pmatrix}$ B $\mathbf{r} = \begin{pmatrix} 1 \\ -2 \\ -3 \end{pmatrix} + \lambda \begin{pmatrix} 0 \\ 3 \\ 2 \end{pmatrix}$

   C $\mathbf{r} = \begin{pmatrix} -1 \\ 3 \\ 5 \end{pmatrix} + \lambda \begin{pmatrix} 1 \\ -2 \\ -3 \end{pmatrix}$ D $\mathbf{r} = \begin{pmatrix} 2 \\ 3 \\ 0 \end{pmatrix} + \lambda \begin{pmatrix} 3 \\ 4 \\ -1 \end{pmatrix}$

3 What is the acute angle between the planes $x + 3y - 4z = 3$ and $3x - 5y - 2z = 4$?

   A $97.3°$ B $82.7°$ C $50.5°$ D $89.8°$

4 What is the point of intersection of the line $\mathbf{r} = \begin{pmatrix} 1 \\ 0 \\ 3 \end{pmatrix} + \lambda \begin{pmatrix} -2 \\ -1 \\ 8 \end{pmatrix}$ and the plane $2x - 2y + z + 1 = 0$?

   A $(3, 1, -5)$ B $(7, 3, -21)$ C $(-1, -1, 11)$ D $(2, 1, -8)$

5 A plane passes through the point $(1, -3, 4)$ and has normal vector $3\mathbf{i} - 2\mathbf{j} - \mathbf{k}$.
   What is the equation of the plane, written in vector form?

   A $\mathbf{r}.(\mathbf{i} - 3\mathbf{j} + 4\mathbf{k}) = 5$ B $\mathbf{r}.(3\mathbf{i} - 2\mathbf{j} - \mathbf{k}) = \mathbf{i} - 3\mathbf{j} + 4\mathbf{k}$

   C $\mathbf{r}.(3\mathbf{i} - 2\mathbf{j} - \mathbf{k}) = 5$ D $\mathbf{r}.(3\mathbf{i} - 2\mathbf{j} - \mathbf{k}) = -7$

Three points $A(1, 2, 0)$, $B(-1, 1, 3)$ and $C(0, 3, -1)$ lie in a plane.

i) Show the vector $2\mathbf{i} + 5\mathbf{j} + 3\mathbf{k}$ is perpendicular to the plane.

ii) Hence find the equation of the plane in cartesian form.

iii) Find the co-ordinates of the point D where the line $\mathbf{r} = \begin{pmatrix} 5 \\ -2 \\ -4 \end{pmatrix} + \lambda \begin{pmatrix} -1 \\ 1 \\ 3 \end{pmatrix}$ crosses the plane.

Differential equations

Separable variables

▶▶ 342
335

A ABOUT THIS TOPIC

An equation involving a derivative such as

$\dfrac{dy}{dx}$, $\dfrac{d^2y}{dx^2}$ or $\dfrac{d\theta}{dt}$ is known as a differential equation.

A first-order differential equation only involves a first

derivative, for example $\dfrac{dy}{dx}$. A differential equation

describes the rates of change of one variable with another. Since this is a common situation, differential equations are very important in mathematics and this work in C4 gives an introduction to them. This section is about solving this kind of equation.

You will be able to solve some of them by direct integration.

Others, such as $\dfrac{dy}{dx} = xy$, $\dfrac{dy}{dx} = \dfrac{x}{y}$, you have to

rearrange first so that one variable is on the left-hand side of the equation and the other on the right-hand side. This is called the method of separation of variables.

R REMEMBER

- Rearranging from GCSE.
- Integration of x^n from C2.
- Integration of $\dfrac{1}{x}$, e^x and trigonometric functions from C3.

- Sketching graphs from C1 and C3.

K KEY POINTS

- Direct integration:

$$\dfrac{dy}{dx} = f(x) \quad \boxed{\text{f is a function of } x.}$$

$$\Rightarrow y = \int f(x)\,dx + c$$

- Method of separation of variables:

$$\dfrac{dy}{dx} = f(x)\,g(y) \quad \boxed{\begin{array}{l}\text{f is a function of } x.\\ \text{g is a function of } y.\end{array}}$$

$$\Rightarrow \int \dfrac{1}{g(y)}\,dy = \int f(x)\,dx \quad \boxed{\begin{array}{l}\text{There will be an arbitrary}\\ \text{constant when you have}\\ \text{carried out the integration.}\end{array}}$$

- The general solution of a differential equation may be represented by a family of curves.

  For example, the general solution for $\dfrac{dy}{dx} = x$ is $y = x^2 + c$.

  So it is family of parabolas. Each curve corresponds to a different value of c, the constant of integration.

- A particular solution is the equation of a single member of the family of curves corresponding to a particular value of c.

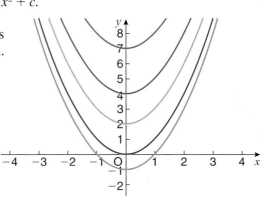

EXAMPLE 1

i) Solve the differential equation $\dfrac{dy}{dx} = x + 3$.

ii) Sketch the family of solution curves, using $c = -2, -1, 0, 1$ and 2.

iii) Find the particular solution for which $y = 9$ when $x = 2$.
Indicate the curve on your graph corresponding to this particular solution.

SOLUTION

i) The right-hand side of the equation is a function of x, so to solve $\dfrac{dy}{dx} = x + 3$, integrate directly.

> y is $\int \dfrac{dy}{dx} dx$ or $\int dy$.

$$y = \int (x + 3)\, dx$$

$$y = \tfrac{1}{2}x^2 + 3x + c$$

> This is the general solution and may be represented by a family of curves.

> Notice that there is one constant and it is on the right-hand side.

ii)

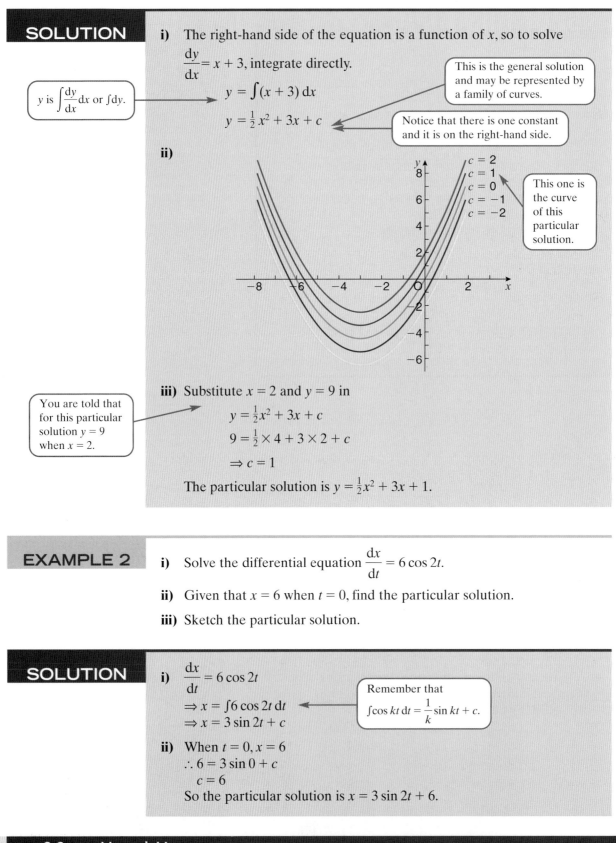

> This one is the curve of this particular solution.

iii) Substitute $x = 2$ and $y = 9$ in

> You are told that for this particular solution $y = 9$ when $x = 2$.

$$y = \tfrac{1}{2}x^2 + 3x + c$$

$$9 = \tfrac{1}{2} \times 4 + 3 \times 2 + c$$

$$\Rightarrow c = 1$$

The particular solution is $y = \tfrac{1}{2}x^2 + 3x + 1$.

EXAMPLE 2

i) Solve the differential equation $\dfrac{dx}{dt} = 6 \cos 2t$.

ii) Given that $x = 6$ when $t = 0$, find the particular solution.

iii) Sketch the particular solution.

SOLUTION

i) $\dfrac{dx}{dt} = 6 \cos 2t$

$$\Rightarrow x = \int 6 \cos 2t\, dt$$
$$\Rightarrow x = 3 \sin 2t + c$$

> Remember that $\int \cos kt\, dt = \dfrac{1}{k} \sin kt + c$.

ii) When $t = 0, x = 6$

$$\therefore 6 = 3 \sin 0 + c$$
$$c = 6$$

So the particular solution is $x = 3 \sin 2t + 6$.

iii) To draw the graph of $x = 3 \sin 2t + 6$, start with $x = \sin t$ and apply:
- a stretch parallel to the t axis; that is, horizontally with factor $\frac{1}{2}$
- a stretch parallel to the x axis; that is, vertically with factor 3
- a translation 6 units upwards.

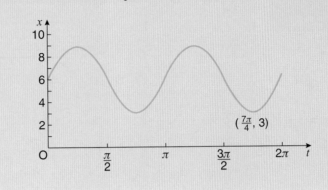

A ADVICE

Differential equations involving sine and cosine are often modelling waves or oscillations as in Example 2.

In the next two examples, the right-hand side contains terms in both x and y. So you have to use the method of separation of variables, getting terms involving x on one side and those involving y on the other.

EXAMPLE 3 Solve $\dfrac{dy}{dx} = xy$ for $y > 0$.

SOLUTION Look at the right-hand side of the equation. There are two variables, x and y. So you cannot integrate directly. The variables have to be separated.

$$\frac{dy}{dx} = xy$$

> First rearrange the equation so y is on the left-hand side.

$$\frac{1}{y}\frac{dy}{dx} = x$$

Now integrate

$$\int \frac{1}{y}\,dy = \int x\,dx$$

$$\ln|y| = \frac{x^2}{2} + c$$

> Notice that c is a part of the power.

> You are told that $y > 0$ so you don't need the modulus signs around y.

$$y = e^{\frac{1}{2}x^2 + c}$$

$$y = e^{\frac{1}{2}x^2} e^c$$

$$y = A e^{\frac{1}{2}x^2}$$

> Notice that e^c is a constant so it is replaced by a new constant A. A is positive.

EXAMPLE 4

i) Find the general solution of $\dfrac{dy}{dx} = \dfrac{\cos x}{3y^2}$.

ii) Find the particular solution for which $y = 1$ when $x = \pi$.

SOLUTION

i) $\quad\dfrac{dy}{dx} = \dfrac{\cos x}{3y^2}$

> First separate the variables.

$\quad 3y^2 \dfrac{dy}{dx} = \cos x$

$\quad \int 3y^2\, dy = \int \cos x\, dx$

$\quad y^3 = \sin x + c$

$\quad y = \sqrt[3]{\sin x + c}$

> Remember that the integral of $\cos kx$ is $\dfrac{1}{k}\sin kx$.

ii) To find the particular solution substitute $x = \pi$ and $y = 1$ in the equation

$\quad y^3 = \sin x + c$

so $\quad 1 = 0 + c$

and the particular solution is $y = \sqrt[3]{\sin x + 1}$

EXAMPLE 5

Find the general solution of $\dfrac{dy}{dx} = \dfrac{y(y-1)}{x}$, for cases where $x > 0$ and $y > 1$.

SOLUTION

Rearrange the equation by separating the variables.

$\quad \dfrac{dy}{dx} = \dfrac{y(y-1)}{x}$

$\quad \dfrac{1}{y(y-1)} \dfrac{dy}{dx} = \dfrac{1}{x}$

$\quad \int \dfrac{1}{y(y-1)}\, dy = \int \dfrac{1}{x}\, dx$

$\quad \int \left(-\dfrac{1}{y} + \dfrac{1}{y-1} \right) dy = \int \dfrac{1}{x}\, dx$

$\quad -\ln y + \ln (y-1) = \ln x + c$

$\quad \ln \dfrac{(y-1)}{y} = \ln x + c$

$\quad \dfrac{y-1}{y} = e^{\ln x + c}$

$\quad 1 - \dfrac{1}{y} = k e^{\ln x}$ where $k = e^c$

$\quad \dfrac{1}{y} = 1 - kx$

$\quad y = \dfrac{1}{1 - kx}$

> Remember that to integrate $\dfrac{1}{y(y-1)}$ you will use partial fractions.
>
> $\dfrac{1}{y(y-1)} = \dfrac{A}{y} + \dfrac{B}{y-1}$
>
> $1 = A(y-1) + By$
>
> $(A+B)y - A = 1$
>
> $\Rightarrow A = -1,\ B = 1$

> Remember the rules of logarithms:
> $\log a - \log b = \log \dfrac{a}{b}$.

> Remember that $e^{\ln x} = x$.

LINKS

Pure Mathematics	Integration and Curve Sketching (C1, C2 & C4).
Mechanics	Motion (M3), Variable Forces and Variable Mass (M4).
Differential Equations	Throughout Differential Equations (DC).

Test Yourself

1 Which of the following is the general solution of the differential equation $\dfrac{dy}{dx} = \sqrt{x} + 3$?

A $y = \dfrac{3}{2}x^{\frac{3}{2}} + 3x + c$

B $y = x^{\frac{3}{2}} + 3x + c$

C $y = \dfrac{2}{3}x^{\frac{3}{2}} + 3x + c$

D $y = \dfrac{2}{3}x^{\frac{3}{2}} + c$

2 Find the general solution of the differential equation $\dfrac{dy}{dx} = x^2 y$, for $y > 0$.

A $y = Ae^{x^3}$

B $y = \dfrac{1}{3}e^{x^3 + c}$

C $y = Ae^{\frac{1}{3}x^3}$

D $y = e^{\frac{1}{3}x^3} + c$

3 Find the particular solution of the differential equation $(x^2 - 3)\dfrac{dy}{dx} = \dfrac{2x}{y}$ for which $y = 2$ when $x = 2$.

A $y = \pm\sqrt{\ln(x^2 - 3)^2 + 4}$

B $y = \ln(x^2 - 3) + 2$

C $y = \sqrt{\ln(x^2 - 3)^2}$

D $y = \sqrt{\ln(x^2 - 3)^2} + 2$

4 Three of the following statements about the differential equation $x\dfrac{dy}{dx} = y^2 - 1$ are false and one is true. Which one is true?

A To integrate $\dfrac{1}{y^2 - 1}$, use partial fractions to write it as $\dfrac{1}{y - 1} - \dfrac{1}{y + 1}$.

B The function $\ln\dfrac{y - 1}{y + 1}$ is defined for all values of y.

C $e^{\ln x^2 + c}$ can be replaced by Ax^2.

D The general solution of this differential equation is $y = \dfrac{1 - Ax^2}{1 + Ax^2}$, $A > 0$.

5 Which of the following graphs is the curve of the particular solution of the differential equation $\dfrac{dy}{dx} = \dfrac{3y}{x}$, $x > 0$ and $y > 0$ for which $y = 1$ when $x = 1$?

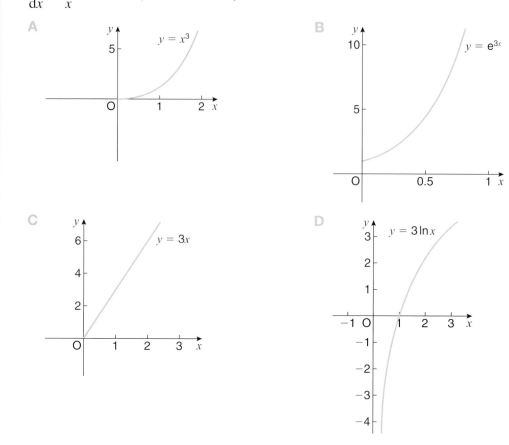

A

$y = x^3$

B

$y = e^{3x}$

C

$y = 3x$

D

$y = 3 \ln x$

Exam-Style Question

i) Find the general solution of the differential equation $\dfrac{dy}{dx} = -xy$, given that $y > 0$.

ii) Sketch the family of solution curves.

iii) The curve of a particular solution passes through the point $(0, 5)$.
Write down its equation.

Formation and interpretation

ABOUT THIS TOPIC

This section is about setting up and interpreting differential equations. Many real-life problems involve the rate of change of a quantity such as temperature, acceleration, velocity and displacement and so give rise to differential equations. The solutions of such equations are used to make predictions about the behaviour of the variables involved.

Several scientific models, such as Newton's law of cooling, and models of growth and decay, can be presented in the form $\dfrac{dx}{dt} = \pm kx$, where k is a positive constant; others are more complicated. Interpretation of such real-life problems and their solutions is an important part of mathematics.

R **REMEMBER**

- Direct and inverse proportion from GCSE.
- Rearranging formulae from GCSE.
- Integration of x^n from C2.
- Integration of $\dfrac{1}{x}$ and e^x from C3.

K **KEY FACTS**

- 'The rate of change of a quantity' usually means 'the rate of change of this quantity with respect to time'. For example, the rate of change of a volume, V, is $\dfrac{dV}{dt}$. The words 'with respect to time' are often omitted.

- Velocity, v, the rate of change of position, s, of an object with respect to time is given by $v = \dfrac{ds}{dt}$.

- In motion along a straight line, the acceleration is the rate of change of an object's velocity:
  $$a = \dfrac{dv}{dt}$$

- It is possible to have a rate of change with respect to another variable. For example, the rate of change of temperature, T, with respect to distance x is $\dfrac{dT}{dx}$.

EXAMPLE 1

A shape has area A at time t. The variables A and t are related by the differential equation $\dfrac{dA}{dt} = k\sqrt{A}$.

i) Explain the meaning of $\dfrac{dA}{dt}$.

ii) What does the differential equation tell you?

SOLUTION

i) $\dfrac{dA}{dt}$ means the rate at which the area, A, is changing with time t.

ii) The differential equation $\dfrac{dA}{dt} = k\sqrt{A}$ tells you that the rate of change of the area A is directly proportional to the square root of the area.

EXAMPLE 2

A small ball is dropped into still water, forming a circular ripple. The radius of the ripple increases at a rate that is inversely proportional to its size. When the radius is 20 cm, the rate of increase of the radius is 2 cm per second.

i) Obtain the differential equation that represents this situation.

ii) The ball has radius 1 cm, so that the initial radius of the ripple is 1 cm.
   (**A**) Solve the differential equation.
   (**B**) Sketch the graph of the radius against time and describe what it shows.
   (**C**) Find the radius half a minute after the ball hits the water.

SOLUTION

i) Start by giving the variables letters.

Let r cm be the radius and t s be the time after the ball hits the water.

You are told that the radius of the circle increases at a rate that is inversely proportional to its size.

$\dfrac{dr}{dt}$ is the rate of increase of r $\dfrac{dr}{dt} = \dfrac{k}{r}$

> k is the constant of proportionality. It is positive because the radius is increasing.

> 'Inversely proportional to r' tells you that r is on the bottom line.

You are also told that when the radius is 20 cm, the rate of increase of the radius is 2 cm per second. Use this information to find the value of k.

It tells you that $\dfrac{dr}{dt} = 2$ when $r = 20$.

Substituting in the equation $\dfrac{dr}{dt} = \dfrac{k}{r}$ gives

$$2 = \dfrac{k}{20}$$

and so $k = 40$.

So the differential equation is $\dfrac{dr}{dt} = \dfrac{40}{r}$.

ii) (**A**) Separating variables

$$\int r \, dr = \int 40 \, dt$$

$$\Rightarrow \tfrac{1}{2}r^2 = 40t + c$$

To find c, use the additional information that when $t = 0, r = 1$. Substituting these values gives

$$\tfrac{1}{2} \times 1^2 = 40 \times 0 + c$$

giving $c = \tfrac{1}{2}$

$$\tfrac{1}{2}r^2 = 40t + \tfrac{1}{2}$$

$$r = \sqrt{80t + 1}$$

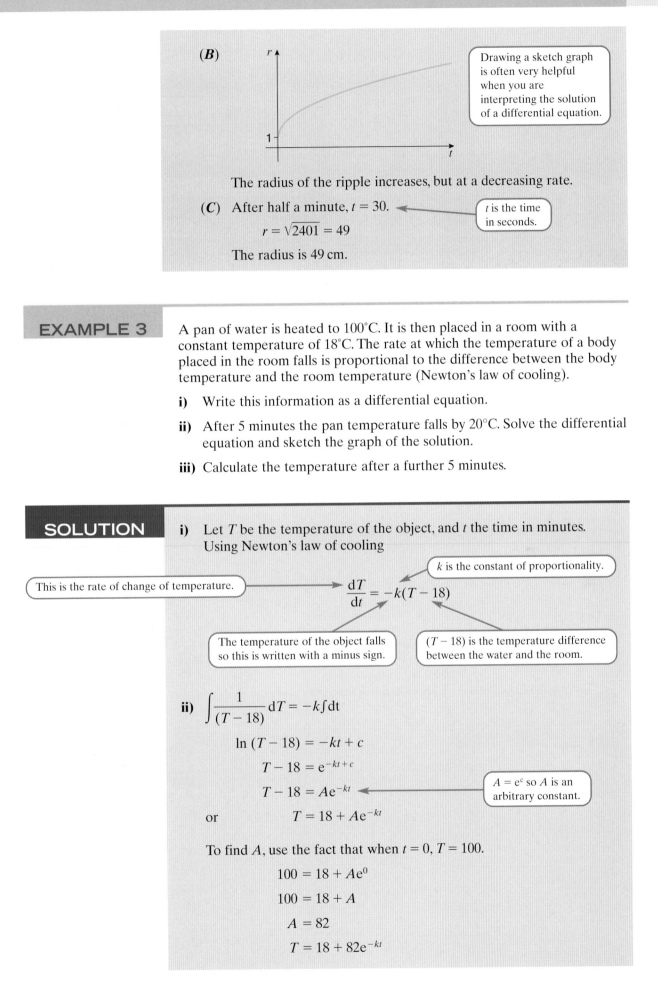

(B)

The radius of the ripple increases, but at a decreasing rate.

(C) After half a minute, $t = 30$. ← *t* is the time in seconds.

$$r = \sqrt{2401} = 49$$

The radius is 49 cm.

EXAMPLE 3

A pan of water is heated to 100°C. It is then placed in a room with a constant temperature of 18°C. The rate at which the temperature of a body placed in the room falls is proportional to the difference between the body temperature and the room temperature (Newton's law of cooling).

i) Write this information as a differential equation.

ii) After 5 minutes the pan temperature falls by 20°C. Solve the differential equation and sketch the graph of the solution.

iii) Calculate the temperature after a further 5 minutes.

SOLUTION

i) Let T be the temperature of the object, and t the time in minutes. Using Newton's law of cooling

k is the constant of proportionality.

This is the rate of change of temperature. →

$$\frac{dT}{dt} = -k(T - 18)$$

The temperature of the object falls so this is written with a minus sign.

$(T - 18)$ is the temperature difference between the water and the room.

ii) $$\int \frac{1}{(T - 18)} \, dT = -k \int dt$$

$$\ln(T - 18) = -kt + c$$

$$T - 18 = e^{-kt + c}$$

$$T - 18 = Ae^{-kt} \quad \leftarrow$$ *$A = e^c$ so A is an arbitrary constant.*

or $$T = 18 + Ae^{-kt}$$

To find A, use the fact that when $t = 0$, $T = 100$.

$$100 = 18 + Ae^0$$

$$100 = 18 + A$$

$$A = 82$$

$$T = 18 + 82e^{-kt}$$

To find k, use the fact that when $t = 5$, $T = 100 - 20 = 80$.

$$80 = 18 + 82e^{-5k}$$

$$80 - 18 = 82e^{-5k}$$

$$e^{5k} = \frac{62}{82}$$

$$\ln(e^{-5k}) = \ln\left(\frac{62}{82}\right)$$

$\frac{62}{82}$ is less than 1, so $\ln\left(\frac{62}{82}\right)$ is negative.

$$-5k = \ln\left(\frac{62}{82}\right)$$

The minus signs have cancelled each other out.

$$k = -\frac{1}{5}\ln\left(\frac{62}{82}\right)$$

$$k = 0.0559\ldots$$

Keep k in your calculator.

So the solution of the equation is $T = 18 + 82e^{-0.559t}$.

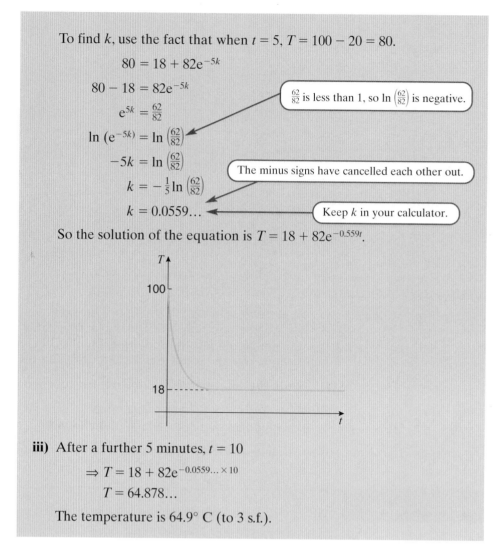

iii) After a further 5 minutes, $t = 10$

$$\Rightarrow T = 18 + 82e^{-0.0559\ldots \times 10}$$

$$T = 64.878\ldots$$

The temperature is $64.9°$ C (to 3 s.f.).

LINKS

Pure Mathematics	Integration and Curve Sketching (C1, C2 & C4).
Mechanics	Motion (M3), Variable Forces and Variable Mass (M4).
Differential Equations	Throughout the module.

Test Yourself ▶L

1 The population of a country increases at a rate that is proportional to the square root of the number of the people present. Which of the following is the differential equation relating the population, x, to the time t?

A $\dfrac{dx}{dt} = kx^2, k > 0$

B $\dfrac{dx}{dt} = k + \sqrt{x}, k > 0$

C $\dfrac{dx}{dt} = k\sqrt{x}, k > 0$

D $\dfrac{dx}{dt} = -k\sqrt{x}, k > 0$

2 An object has velocity v m s^{-1} at time t seconds. Its acceleration is proportional to the cube of its velocity and in the negative direction. Which one of these differential equations models the situation?

A $\dfrac{dv}{dt} = -k + v^3, k > 0$

B $-\dfrac{dv}{dt} = k\sqrt[3]{v}, k > 0$

C $\dfrac{dv}{dt} = -kv^3, k > 0$

D $\dfrac{dt}{dv} = -kv^3, k > 0$

3 Kate starts on a diet. Her weight, w kg after t days, decreases at a rate which is inversely proportional to the square root of her weight. Given that k is a positive constant, one of the following differential equations models this situation. Which one is the correct differential equation?

A $\dfrac{dw}{dt} = \dfrac{k}{\sqrt{w}}, k > 0$

B $\dfrac{dw}{dt} = -\dfrac{k}{\sqrt{w}}, k > 0$

C $\dfrac{dw}{dt} = -\dfrac{k}{w^2}, k > 0$

D $\dfrac{dt}{dw} = -k\sqrt{w}, k > 0$

4 A curve has equation $y = f(x)$. The gradient function of the curve is inversely proportional to the cube of x. The curve passes through $(1, 0)$ and $(2, 3)$.

Find the equation of the curve.

A $y = 4 - \dfrac{4}{x^2}$

B $y = \dfrac{12}{x^2}$

C $5y = x^4 - 1$

D $y = 1 - \dfrac{1}{x^2}$

5 This sketch graph shows the solution of a differential equation connecting P and t, for $t > 0$.

Three of the following statements are false and one is true. Which one is true?

A The equation of the solution could be $P = 1 + 0.1\sqrt{t}$.

B P decays exponentially.

C For larger values of t, P may start to decrease in value.

D The differential equation could be $\dfrac{dP}{dt} = 0.5P(2 - P)$.

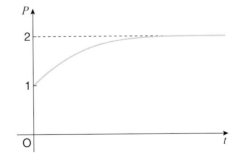

Exam-Style Question ▶L

A quantity of oil is dropped into water. When the oil hits the water, it spreads out as a circle. The radius of the circle is r cm after t seconds. When $t = 0$, $r = 0$ and when $t = 3$ the radius of the circle is increasing at the rate of 0.5 cm s^{-1}.

One observer believes that the radius increases at a rate which is proportional to $\dfrac{1}{(t+1)}$.

i) Write down a differential equation to model this situation, using k as the constant of proportionality.

ii) Show that $k = 2$.

iii) Solve the differential equation and hence calculate the radius of the circle after 10 seconds according to this model.

Another observer suggests that the rate of increase of the radius of the circle is proportional to $\dfrac{1}{(t+1)(t+2)}$.

iv) Write down a new differential equation for this model. Using the same initial conditions as before, find the value of the new constant of proportionality.

v) Hence solve the differential equation.

vi) Calculate the radius of the circle after 10 seconds according to this model.

Index

Formulae and results

Here are some formulae and results which you will need to recall or derive for the C4 examination. You are also expected to recall or derive C1, C2 and C3 results that are not given in the examination booklet. The following list is not exhaustive, and you should check with your teacher before your examination.

Trigonometry

$\sec^2 \theta \equiv 1 + \tan^2 \theta$

$\mathrm{cosec}^2 \theta \equiv 1 + \cot^2 \theta$

$\sin 2\theta = 2 \sin \theta \cos \theta$

$\cos 2\theta = \cos^2 \theta - \sin^2 \theta = 2 \cos^2 \theta - 1 = 1 - 2 \sin^2 \theta$

$\tan 2\theta = \dfrac{2 \tan \theta}{1 - \tan^2 \theta}$

Vectors

$$\begin{pmatrix} u_1 \\ u_2 \\ u_3 \end{pmatrix} \cdot \begin{pmatrix} v_1 \\ v_2 \\ v_3 \end{pmatrix} = u_1 v_1 + u_2 v_2 + u_3 v_3$$